A BOOK OF SCIENCE VERSE

A Book of Science Verse

THE POETIC RELATIONS
OF SCIENCE AND
TECHNOLOGY

Selected by

W. EASTWOOD, M.A.
Vice-Principal
Reading Technical College

LONDON
MACMILLAN & CO LTD
1961

MACMILLAN AND COMPANY LIMITED
London Bombay Calcutta Madras Melbourne

THE MACMILLAN COMPANY OF CANADA LIMITED
Toronto

PRINTED IN GREAT BRITAIN

For JEAN
and
ANDREW and SUSAN

PREFACE

POETRY and science have been regarded by some as antithetical, mutually exclusive. It should be borne in mind, however, that this is a notion of quite recent origin ; it does not go back much further than the late eighteenth century. It is a notion in which I believe there is no truth.

Poet and scientist are alike concerned with the ordering of experience and to both the imagination is all-important. Philosophers have much to say about 'scientific method'; but the great discoverers in science and technology speak not of scientific method but of having an idea, a leap of imagination, an inspiration, the truth or practicability of which they later proceeded to demonstrate. Poetry originates in the same way ; in an intense imaginative experience elaborated later 'in tranquillity'. And poetry and science have more in common in subject-matter than might be supposed. Science is wrongly regarded if it is thought of as a coldly impersonal activity. It is, and was formerly called, natural philosophy, a philosophic instrument for the enlarging of man's understanding of himself and his universe, with its own aesthetic values of orderliness, beauty, truth. It is to-day recognised as an integral part of our culture and perhaps the western world's most important and characteristic contribution to modern civilisation.

How then can poets ignore it ? How can we speak of science or technology as unpoetic ? Poetry is concerned with life, in which science plays an all-important part ; and in fact most poets have taken science into account in their personal philosophies and in their views of society. Their distress, where it was warranted, at the impact of science on belief and on society has been shared by the scientists themselves. Concern at the misuse of scientific and technological discovery has not been the monopoly of the poet, any more than has rejoicing at the success of the human intellect in the scientific field been the monopoly of the scientist.

This anthology includes complete poems, and extracts from longer poems, from many periods, and of many different forms and types and styles and moods, all nevertheless relating directly to science or technology. In their own way, and in small compass, they mirror the history of human culture and ideas, and the unity of knowledge. Such poetry will continue to be written and increasingly so, for a poetry which ignores science and its applications is, in the modern world, divorced from life ; just as a science in which imagination has no part is sterile or dead. There is no future for a culture which cannot reconcile the poetic and scientific impulses, for both are necessary to the human spirit.

I have tried to make this collection as representative as possible. In so doing I have included a few pieces of light verse, some of which may seem as doubtful poetically as others are manifestly genuine poetry. I have tried to get the broadest possible survey within the limits at my disposal, and this has meant ranging from the sublime to the burlesque and back to the sublime. I should have liked to include James Kirkup's 'A Correct Compassion', a poem for which I have a very great admiration, but I was unfortunately unable to obtain copyright permission in this case.

Anthologists cannot hope to please all : but I hope that this collection may please some in both the scientific and the literary worlds. If it brings individuals in those spheres of our present society even a little closer together, that will be ample enough reward.

W. E.

ACKNOWLEDGMENTS

THE editor and publishers wish to acknowledge their indebtedness to the following, who have kindly given permission for the use of copyright material : Professor W. H. Auden and Messrs. Faber & Faber, Ltd., for 'The Unknown Citizen', from *Another Time*, 'In Memory of Sigmund Freud', from *Collected Shorter Poems 1930–1944*, and 'Ode to Gaea', from *The Shield of Achilles* ; Mrs. George Bambridge, for 'The Secret of the Machines' and 'Hymn of Breaking Strain', from *The Definitive Edition of Rudyard Kipling's Verse* ; Mrs. George Bambridge and Messrs. Methuen & Co., Ltd., for 'M'Andrew's Hymn', from *The Seven Seas*, by Rudyard Kipling ; the Representatives of the late Hilaire Belloc and Messrs. Gerald Duckworth & Co., Ltd., for 'Newdigate Poem : The Benefits of the Electric Light', from *Sonnets and Verse* ; Mr. Edmund Blunden, for 'The Scientists', from *Poems 1930–1940* ; The Bodley Head, Ltd., for 'The Submarine', from *Lyrics and Dramas*, by Stephen Phillips, and 'To Iron-Founders and Others', from *Poems of Thirty Years*, by Gordon Bottomley ; Dr. J. Bronowski and Messrs. William Heinemann, Ltd., for the extract from *The Common Sense of Science* ; the Syndics of the Cambridge University Press, for 'New Ballad of Sir Patrick Spens', from *From a Cornish Window*, by Sir Arthur Quiller-Couch, and the extract from *Science and the Modern World*, by A. N. Whitehead ; Mr. Robert Conquest, for 'Guided Missiles Experimental Range', from *Poems*, and 'For the 1956 Opposition of Mars' ; Mr. Cecil Day Lewis, for 'Flight to Australia', from *A Time to Dance, and Other Poems*, and the extract from *A Hope for Poetry* ; the Literary Trustees of Walter de la Mare and The Society of Authors as their representative, for 'The Dunce', from *Inward Companion* ; Messrs. J. M. Dent & Sons, Ltd., for 'The Force that through the Green Fuse drives the Flower', from *18 Poems*, by Dylan Thomas ; Mr. Patric Dickinson and Messrs. Chatto & Windus, Ltd., for 'Jodrell Bank' and 'On Dow Crag', from *The World I See* ; the Trustees of the Hardy Estate, for 'At a Lunar Eclipse' and 'Heredity', from *The Collected Poems of Thomas*

Hardy; Mr. Aldous Huxley and Messrs. Chatto & Windus, Ltd., for 'Fifth Philosopher's Song', from *Leda*; Mr. E. V. Knox and Messrs. Methuen & Co., Ltd., for 'The Steam-Givers', from *These Liberties*; the Estate of the late Mrs. Frieda Lawrence, for 'The Triumph of the Machine', from *The Complete Poems of D. H. Lawrence*, published by Messrs. William Heinemann, Ltd.; Messrs. John Murray (Publishers), Ltd., for 'Success in Malaria Research', by Sir Ronald Ross; the Representatives of the Estate of the late Dr. Alfred Noyes, for 'The Observatory', from *The Torch-Bearers*, Vol. I; Miss Kathleen Raine and Messrs. Hamish Hamilton, Ltd., for 'The Human Form Divine' and 'Rock', from *The Collected Poems*; Mr. I. A. Richards and Messrs. Routledge & Kegan Paul, Ltd., for the extract from *Science and Poetry*; Messrs. Routledge & Kegan Paul, Ltd., for 'Greenwich Observatory', from *The Cruel Solstice*, by Sidney Keyes; Mr. Stanley Snaith, for 'Pylons', from *The Silver Scythe*; Mr. Stephen Spender and Messrs. Faber & Faber, Ltd., for 'The Funeral', 'The Express', 'The Landscape near an Aerodrome' and 'The Pylons', from *Poems*; Mr. Raglan Squire, for 'In Continuation of Pope on Newton', from *Collected Poems of Sir John Squire*; Mr. A. S. J. Tessimond, for 'La Marche des Machines'; and Mr. John Wain, for 'Poem Feigned to have been written by an Electronic Brain', from *A Word Carved on a Sill*, published by Messrs. Routledge & Kegan Paul, Ltd. 'Power' is taken from *The Collected Poems of Hart Crane*, by permission of Liveright, Publishers, New York, N.Y. Copyright (R) 1961 by Liveright Publishing Corporation. 'New Farm Tractor' is taken from *Smoke and Steel*, by Carl Sandburg, copyright, 1920, by Harcourt Brace and Company, Inc.; copyright, 1948, by Carl Sandburg. Reprinted by permission of the publishers. 'Mr. Attila' is taken from *Complete Poems*, by Carl Sandburg, copyright, 1950, by Carl Sandburg. Reprinted by permission of Harcourt, Brace and Company, Inc. 'Overture to a Dance of Locomotives' is taken from *The Collected Earlier Poems of William Carlos Williams* and is reprinted by permission of New Directions. Copyright 1938, 1951 by William Carlos Williams.

In three cases the publishers have been unable to trace the copyright-holders, but they will be pleased to make the necessary arrangements at the first opportunity.

CONTENTS

PAGE

Contents

A Book of Science Verse

Contents

ATOMIC THEORY

Now for the rest lend me attentive ears
And turn a piercing mind not burdened down with cares
To true philosophy.
I would not have these gifts of mine
Set out for you with constant, faithful zeal,
Disdained before they're understood.
For I propose to tell
The highest laws of heaven and the gods,
Reveal the primal stuff of things
And show how from this primaeval atom stuff
Creative nature forms all things, and grows and nurtures
     them ;
To which again
This same creative nature breaks them up and sends them
     back.
And this in our account we call
Matter, creative stuff of things or seeds of things,
Or primal bodies, some might say,
Because from these as elementary principles
Emerge all things that are.

.   .   .   .   .

Now more in atoms which our sense can never grasp,
There is a series of irreducible points,
Of which each point, we may be sure,
Is indivisible and very small.
It never has existed by itself nor will it ever come to be alone,
Since every atom form exists
A primary and single part
Of some thing else.
And other atom parts and others yet in close array,

Make up the nature of the thing.
Since by themselves they cannot stand alone,
They needs must cling to other atom forms,
And from this unity cannot be torn.
And so the atoms are of solid singleness,
A close dense mass of tiny parts
Not put together by a union of the parts
But rather always strong in solid singleness.
From these atomic forms,
Nature, keeping safe the seeds of things,
Will not allow that anything should be removed or torn away.
Unless there were these atoms, infinitely small,
Then smallest things would be composed
Of countless parts.
For half of half will always have a half,
And so on to infinity.
And then what difference would there be,
Between the least and greatest thing ?
Why none at all.
For though the sum of things were infinite,
Yet smallest things would yet have parts,
In number infinite.
But this the reason never could accept
And will not let the mind believe.

·   ·   ·   ·   ·

So those who thought that fire's the substance of the universe,
From fire the sum of things was made,
And those who think that air performs this role,
Or those who think that moisture alone has fashioned every-
        thing,
Or those who think that earth created everything
And took the form of all created things
All these have wandered very far from truth.
And those who posit two first principles
Add air to fire, to moisture earth,
I blame them equally.
And also those who think from four first principles

Have all things come —
From earth and air, from moisture and fire
They're just as wrong.

.   .   .   .   .

If all created things are held to come from four first principles
To these again are held to be resolved,
How can these four be called first principles of things
Rather than things of them ?
For they're created turn by turn, their colours change
And all their nature, too, from endless time.
But if you think corporeal forms of fire
And earth and breeze and moisture so unite
That in this union none of them are changed,
Then you will see that nothing could be made from them,
No living thing, no lifeless body — like a tree.
Rather in such a union of things unlike
Each will reveal itself, show its true self.
Air will be seen as mixed with earth ; moisture with heat.
But in begetting things
The elements should bring to bear a secret unseen form
That nothing might stand out or fight against the union,
Or stop created thing from achieving its new form.
But as it is you see
They trace it back to sky and fires of sky
Assume that fire can turn itself into the winds of sky,
That thence comes rain, and earth can come from rain.
And then again the process in reverse —
That from the earth can come,
First moisture, then the air, and then the heat.
But elemental principles should not behave like this.
There must be something that abides unchangeable
In order that the sum of things should not be brought to
     nothingness.
For whatsoe'er is changed, beyond its limit goes
This straightway is the death of that which went before.
Now since the things we've named above are subject to
     exchange

3

It's clear they must be made from other things
Which cannot change or alteration find,
Or else you'd find all things return to nothingness.
Were it not better to assume atomic forms ?
And if from these by chance the fire were made,
Adding a few and taking some away,
Their movement and their order changed
Then air results.
And so with this hypothesis
All things can change themselves to other things
Because all come from atoms.
But Memmius, you may argue thus ;
'The patent facts of things reveal
That all things grow, are nurtured from the earth,
And rise to meet the breezes ;
Unless when time of year is right the rain abounds,
That shrubs and trees are pelted with the stress of storm,
Unless the sun will warm and cherish them,
Then crops and trees and animals alike,
Could never grow.'
Yes and it's true,
Unless dry food, soft moisture, too, assisted human kind,
We, too, should die, would lose our flesh,
And all the life be loosened from our sinews and our bones.
Assuredly we're nourished and we're nurtured by fixed
elements.
All other species, too, kind after kind.
Of this we may be sure
It's just because atomic elements
Common so many ways to many things
Are mixed in things,
That all the various species all are fed on divers foods.
And often it's a matter of profound significance
With just what atoms other atoms join,
And how they're placed, arranged,
What motions they receive, transmit among themselves ;
Because, you see,
From these atomic shapes are built so many things,

4

Sky and the sea and earth,
Rivers and sun and crops and trees and living things,
In various movements, various mixtures linked.
It's just the same in all these verses that you read.
Scattered throughout the whole are letters — in number
    infinite,
And yet you have to grant that words and verse alike
Will differ widely both in sense and power of sound.
Majestic is the power of letters when their order's changed.
But atoms bring to bear wider variety,
And so create,
A rich and infinitely wide diversity of things.

From LUCRETIUS, *De Rerum Natura*, Book I (*c.* 55 B.C.),
translated by A. D. Winspear (1956)

EVOLUTION AND THE ORIGINS OF LIFE

Now I come back and tell of early days on earth,
And earth's soft fields ;
And what the earth resolved in earliest pangs of birth
To bring to shining shores of light, entrust to gusty winds.
In early times, then, earth brought forth the varying kinds of
    grass
And foliage glowing green on all the hills around and over
    every plain,
And flowery meadows flamed in radiance of green.
And then to various shrubs was given the power to leap into
    the air,
Like race horse on the track when reins are loosed.
And as on any fledgling four legged beast
Or strong winged bird of air,
Bristles and down and hair are formed,
So earth, new-born raised herbs and shrubbery first,
And then produced the tribes of living things —
Those various tribes that came to be

So variously in many ways.
For living creatures could not fall from sky,
Nor land born creatures leap from salty sea.
And so we must conclude that man was right
To call the earth his mother,
For from this mother earth were all things made.
Even today many creatures spring from earth,
Nurtured by rains and warming heat of sun.
And so it is not wonderful if when the earth was young and
     sky was fresh
More creatures sprang from earth and larger creatures than
     the ones we know ;
And, after birth, grew great and strong and reached
     maturity.
For first the wingéd fowl and all the birds
Emerged from eggs, were hatched in spring,
Even as now the grasshoppers
In summer leave their shapely shells spontaneously
To seek for life and livelihood.
And then the earth brought forth the mortal generations of
     all living things.
For in the early days of earth, moisture and heat abounded in
     the fields.
And thus wherever place seemed suitable, there sprang up
     female wombs
Which with their tentacles clung to the earth ;
And when the time was fully ripe the tiny offsprings opened
     these
In flight from moisture and in search of air ;
And where the tiny things appeared
Mother Nature turned the pores of earth
And from their open veins compelled a sap to flow
Most like the flow of milk.
Just as even now when women bring a child to birth
They fill with milk ;
Because the pressure of their nourishment is turned towards
     the breasts.
And for these new-born tiny things

Earth gave forth food,
While warmth gave raiment
And the grass a bed, abounding with a wealth of soft and
    gentle down.
But earth was young and so did not produce
Hard frosts, excessive heat or over violent winds.
For all things grow alike, alike put on their strength.
And so again, I say, it's right,
That earth should gain and keep the name of Mother.
Since every creature — man and beast alike
She brings to birth — when time is ripe,
The beasts that revel everywhere on lofty hills,
And all the birds of air with all their varying forms.

.   .   .   .   .

It must have been that in the early days of earth
Countless kinds of living things died out
And failed to reproduce their kind.
For all the living things you now see feeding on the breath of
    life
Must have survived, after the first appearance of their kind,
Either through cunning or through valour or through speed
    of foot.
And many kinds have proved their usefulness to human
    kind,
Have lived and thrived
Because entrusted to the care of man.
The fierce and savage race of lions through valour has
    survived ;
Foxes through cunning and the deer through speed.
But lightly sleeping loyal dogs,
The beasts of burden, fleecy flocks and hornéd kine
Are all, my friend, entrusted to the care of man.
Gladly they shunned the life of savage beasts
And sought domestic peace ;
And bounteous fodder these have gained without the toil of
    raising it —
The fodder which men give to various animals

7

To reward their usefulness to us.
To some has nature given neither way of life —
Survival by themselves spontaneously nor usefulness to man.
For which we let them live and feed, be safe, survive,
Under our kindly guardianship.
And these fell spoil and prey to other kinds
All caught in trammels of their luckless destiny
Until the time when nature had destroyed their race.

     .   .   .   .   .

The human race was harder far in early days than now,
As you'd expect, since hard earth brought it forth.
Its bones within were harder, solider ;
Its sinews binding flesh were tougher far.
Its hardy strength could hardly be assailed by heat or cold
Or novel food or any flaw in human frame.
Age after age while sun sped through the sky
They lived their life like wandering beasts.
No sturdy ploughman held his curving plough ;
No skill was theirs to till the fields with iron share,
Or plant young shoots in earth,
Or prune high trees with knives.
The gift of sun and showers, spontaneous bounty of the earth,
Was boon enough to please their hearts.
Under the acorn-laden oaks they gained their sustenance ;
Or dined on berried arbute
(These you've seen in winter red ;
Much larger were they in the days of old.)
Besides all this the flowering youth of earth
Bore other fare as rough, plenty for wretched men.
To quench their thirst the rills and rivers called,
As now from mighty hills the water's fall
In loud and solemn tones calls thirsty roving beasts.
Or in their wandering they came to know
The woodland church of nymphs and lingered there.
For they knew
That water gliding there in bounteous flood
Washed the wet rocks and trickled over mosses green,

And sometimes welled and burst its banks
And rushed o'er level plain.
Not yet did man know how to serve himself with fire.
He had not thought to clothe himself with skins,
Use spoils of chase for body's covering.
Men dwelt in woods and glades and hollow mountain caves ;
And hid their shaggy limbs in brushwood piles
When blows of wind or rain forced them to hide.
They could not think of social good
Or know the fine restraint of common codes or laws.
Whatever booty fortune gave the individual seized,
His only learning was to live and thrive himself.

. . . . .

And when as time went on, men came to master fire,
Gained themselves huts and skins to cover them,
One man, one woman in a single hut together lived,
And tiny ones around them growing up they saw,
Then first the human race learned gentler ways.
Now used to fire
Their freezing limbs would shrink from cold beneath the
    vault of sky.
Excessive sex wore down their savage strength,
And children with their blandishments
Subdued their elder's haughty will.
Then neighbour oft to neighbour pledged his word
Eager to form a friendship and refrain from mutual harm.
And pity they'd evoke for girls and children, too,
When these with piteous cries,
Pathetic gestures and the broken word
Would teach the primal law of moral life
That all should spare the weak.
Yet concord was a lesson hard to learn.
Most of mankind was loyal to its pledge.
Else would the human race in earliest times have failed
Nor wealth of progeny sufficed destruction to avert.

From LUCRETIUS, *De Rerum Natura*, Book V (*c.* 55 B.C.),
translated by A. D. Winspear (1956)

THE STRUCTURE OF THE UNIVERSE

ALL ye, who in small bark have following sail'd,
Eager to listen, on the adventurous track
Of my proud keel, that singing cuts her way,
Backward return with speed, and your own shores
Revisit ; nor put out to open sea,
Where losing me, perchance ye may remain
Bewilder'd in deep maze. The way I pass,
Ne'er yet was run : Minerva breathes the gale ;
Apollo guides me ; and another Nine,
To my rapt sight, the arctic beams reveal.
Ye other few who have outstretch'd the neck
Timely for food of angels, on which here
They live, yet never know satiety ;
Through the deep brine ye fearless may put out
Your vessel ; marking well the furrow broad
Before you in the wave, that on both sides
Equal returns. Those, glorious, who pass'd o'er
To Colchis, wonder'd not as ye will do,
When they saw Jason following the plough.
    The increate perpetual thirst, that draws
Toward the realm of God's own form, bore us
Swift almost as the Heaven ye behold.
    Beatrice upward gazed, and I on her ;
And in such space as on the notch a dart
Is placed, then loosen'd flies, I saw myself
Arrived, where wonderous thing engaged my sight.
Whence she, to whom no care of mine was hid,
Turning to me, with aspect glad as fair,
Bespake me : 'Gratefully direct thy mind
To God, through whom to this first star we come.'
    Meseem'd as if a cloud had cover'd us,
Translucent, solid, firm, and polish'd bright,
Like adamant, which the sun's beam had smit.
Within itself the ever-during pearl
Received us ; as the wave a ray of light

Receives, and rests unbroken. If I then
Was of corporeal frame, and it transcend
Our weaker thought, how one dimension thus
Another could endure, which needs must be
If body enter body ; how much more
Must the desire inflame us to behold
That Essence, which discovers by what means
God and our nature join'd ! There will be seen
That, which we hold through faith ; not shown
    by proof,
But in itself intelligibly plain,
E'en as the truth that man at first believes.
    I answer'd : 'Lady ! I with thoughts devout,
Such as I best can frame, give thanks to Him,
Who hath removed me from the mortal world.
But tell, I pray thee, whence the gloomy spots
Upon this body, which below on earth
Give rise to talk of Cain in fabling quaint ?'
    She somewhat smiled, then spake : 'If mortals err
In their opinion, when the key of sense
Unlocks not, surely wonder's weapon keen
Ought not to pierce thee : since thou find'st the
    wings
Of reason to pursue the senses' flight
Are short. But what thy own thought is, declare.'
    Then I : 'What various here above appears,
Is caused, I deem, by bodies dense or rare.'
    She then resumed : 'Thou certainly wilt see
In falsehood thy belief o'erwhelm'd, if well
Thou listen to the arguments which I
Shall bring to face it. The eighth sphere displays
Numberless lights, the which, in kind and size,
May be remark'd of different aspects :
If rare or dense of that were cause alone,
One single virtue then would be in all ;
Alike distributed, or more, or less.
Different virtues needs must be the fruits
Of formal principles ; and these, save one,

Will by thy reasoning be destroy'd. Beside,
If rarity were of that dusk the cause,
Which thou inquirest, either in some part
That planet must throughout be void, nor fed
With its own matter ; or, as bodies share
Their fat and leanness, in like manner this
Must in its volume change the leaves. The first,
If it were true, had through the sun's eclipse
Been manifested, by transparency
Of light, as through aught rare beside effused.
But this is not. Therefore remains to see
The other cause : and, if the other fall,
Erroneous so must prove what seem'd to thee.
If not from side to side this rarity
Pass through, there needs must be a limit, whence
Its contrary no further lets it pass.
And hence the beam, that from without proceeds,
Must be pour'd back ; as colour comes, through glass
    glass
Reflected, which behind it lead conceals.
Now wilt thou say, that there of murkier hue,
Than, in the other part, the ray is shown,
By being thence refracted farther back.
From this perplexity will free thee soon
Experience, if thereof thou trial make,
The fountain whence your arts derive their streams.
Three mirrors shalt thou take, and two remove
From thee alike ; and more remote the third,
Betwixt the former pair, shall meet thine eyes :
Then turn'd toward them, cause behind thy back
A light to stand, that on the three shall shine,
And thus reflected come to thee from all.
Though that, beheld most distant, do not stretch
A space so ample, yet in brightness thou
Wilt own it equaling the rest. But now,
As under snow the ground, if the warm ray
Smites it, remains dismantled of the hue
And cold, that cover'd it before ; so thee,

Dismantled in thy mind, I will inform
With light so lively, that the tremulous beam
Shall quiver where it falls. Within the Heaven,
Where peace divine inhabits, circles round
A body, in whose virtue lies the being
Of all that it contains. The following Heaven,
That hath so many lights, this being divides,
Through different essences, from it distinct,
And yet contain'd within it. The other orbs
Their separate distinctions variously
Dispose, for their own seed and produce apt.
Thus do these organs of the world proceed,
As thou beholdest now, from step to step ;
Their influences from above deriving,
And thence transmitting downwards. Mark me
    well ;
How through this passage to the truth I ford,
The truth thou lovest ; that thou henceforth, alone,
Mayst know to keep the shallows, safe, untold.
  'The virtue and motion of the sacred orbs,
As mallet by the workman's hand, must needs
By blessed movers be inspired. This Heaven,
Made beauteous by so many luminaries,
From the deep spirit, that moves its circling
    sphere,
Its image takes and impress as a seal :
And as the soul, that dwells within your dust,
Through members different, yet together form'd,
In different powers resolves itself ; e'en so
The intellectual efficacy unfolds
Its goodness multiplied throughout the stars ;
On its own unity revolving still.
Different virtue compact different
Makes with the precious body it enlivens,
With which it knits, as life in you is knit.
From its original nature full of joy,
The virtue mingled through the body shines,
As joy through pupil of the living eye.

From hence proceeds that which from light to light
Seems different, and not from dense or rare.
This is the formal cause, that generates,
Proportion'd to its power, the dusk or clear.'

Dante Alighieri, *Commedia* : *Paradiso*, Canto II (*c.* 1320),
translated by H. F. Cary (1814)

A PHYSICIAN

With us ther was a Doctour of Phisyk,
In al this world ne was ther noon him lyk
To speke of phisik and of surgerye ;
For he was grounded in astronomye.
He kepte his pacient a ful greet del
In houres, by his magik naturel.
Wel coude he fortunen the ascendent
Of his images for his pacient.
He knew the cause of everich maladye,
Were it of hoot or cold, or moiste, or drye,
And where engendred, and of what humour ;
He was a verrey parfit practisour.
The cause y-knowe, and of his harm the rote,
Anon he yaf the seke man his bote.
Ful redy hadde he his apothecaries,
To sende him drogges and his letuaries,
For ech of hem made other for to winne ;
Hir frendschipe nas nat newe to biginne.
Wel knew he th'olde Esculapius,
And Deiscorides, and eek Rufus,
Old Ypocras, Haly, and Galien ;
Serapion, Razis, and Avicen ;
Averrois, Damascien, and Constantyn ;
Bernard, and Gatesden, and Gilbertyn.
Of his diete mesurable was he,
For it was of no superfluitee,

But of greet norissing and digestible.
His studie was but litel on the bible.
In sangwin and in pers he clad was al,
Lyned with taffata and with sendal ;
And yet he was but esy of dispence ;
He kepte that he wan in pestilence.
For gold in phisik is a cordial,
Therfore he lovede gold in special.

From GEOFFREY CHAUCER, *Canterbury Tales :*
Prologue (*c.* 1387)

ALCHEMY

WITH this chanoun I dwelt have seven yeer,
And of his science am I never the neer.
Al that I hadde, I have y-lost ther-by ;
And god wot, so hath many mo than I.
Ther I was wont to be right fresh and gay
Of clothing and of other good array,
Now may I were an hose upon myn heed ;
And wher my colour was bothe fresh and reed,
Now is it wan and of a leden hewe ;
Who-so it useth, sore shal he rewe.
And of my swink yet blered is myn yë,
Lo ! which avantage is to multiplye !
That slyding science hath me maad so bare,
That I have no good, wher that ever I fare ;
And yet I am endetted so ther-by
Of gold that I have borwed, trewely,
That whyl I live, I shal it quyte never.
Lat every man be war by me for ever !
What maner man that casteth him ther-to,
If he continue, I holde his thrift y-do.
So helpe me god, ther-by shal he nat winne,
But empte his purs, and make his wittes thinne.

And whan he, thurgh his madnes and folye,
Hath lost his owene good thurgh jupartye,
Thanne he excyteth other folk ther-to,
To lese hir good as he him-self hath do.
For unto shrewes joye it is and ese
To have hir felawes in peyne and disese ;
Thus was I ones lerned of a clerk.
Of that no charge, I wol speke of our werk.

    Whan we been ther as we shul exercyse
Our elvish craft, we semen wonder wyse,
Our termes been so clergial and so queynte.
I blowe the fyr til that myn herte feynte.

    What sholde I tellen ech proporcioun
Of thinges whiche that we werche upon,
As on fyve or sixe ounces, may wel be,
Of silver or som other quantitee,
And bisie me to telle yow the names
Of orpiment, brent bones, yren squames,
That into poudre grounden been ful smal?
And in an erthen potte how put is al,
And salt y-put in, and also papeer,
Biforn thise poudres that I speke of heer,
And wel y-covered with a lampe of glas,
And mochel other thing which that ther was ?
And of the pot and glasses enluting,
That of the eyre mighte passe out no-thing ?
And of the esy fyr and smart also,
Which that was maad, and of the care and wo
That we hadde in our matires sublyming,
And in amalgaming and calcening
Of quik-silver, y-clept Mercurie crude ?
For alle our sleightes we can nat conclude.
Our orpiment and sublymed Mercurie,
Our grounden litarge eek on the porphurie,
Of ech of thise of ounces a certeyn
Nought helpeth us, our labour is in veyn.
Ne eek our spirites ascencioun,

Ne our materes that lyen al fixe adoun,
Mowe in our werking no-thing us avayle.
For lost is al our labour and travayle,
And al the cost, a twenty devel weye,
Is lost also, which we upon it leye.
    Ther is also ful many another thing
That is unto our craft apertening ;
Though I by ordre hem nat reherce can,
By-cause that I am a lewed man,
Yet wol I telle hem as they come to minde,
Though I ne can nat sette hem in hir kinde ;
As bole armoniak, verdegrees, boras,
And sondry vessels maad of erthe and glas,
Our urinales and our descensories,
Violes, croslets, and sublymatories,
Cucurbites, and alembykes eek,
And othere swiche, dere y-nough a leek.
Nat nedeth it for to reherce hem alle,
Watres rubifying and boles galle,
Arsenik, sal armoniak, and brimstoon ;
And herbes coude I telle eek many oon,
As egremoine, valerian, and lunarie,
And othere swiche, if that me liste tarie.
Our lampes brenning bothe night and day,
To bringe aboute our craft, if that we may.
Our fourneys eek of calcinacioun,
And of watres albificacioun,
Unslekked lym, chalk, and gleyre of an ey,
Poudres diverse, asshes, dong, pisse, and cley,
Cered pokets, sal peter, vitriole ;
And divers fyres maad of wode and cole ;
Sal tartre, alkaly, and sal preparat,
And combust materes and coagulat,
Cley maad with hors or mannes heer, and oile
Of tartre, alum, glas, berm, wort, and argoile,
Resalgar, and our materes enbibing ;
And eek of our materes encorporing,
And of our silver citrinacioun,

Our cementing and fermentacioun,
Our ingottes, testes, and many mo.
   I wol yow telle, as was me taught also,
The foure spirites and the bodies sevene,
By ordre, as ofte I herde my lord hem nevene,
The firste spirit quik-silver called is,
The second orpiment, the thridde, y-wis,
Sal armoniak, and the ferthe brimstoon.
The bodies sevene eek, lo ! hem heer anoon :
Sol gold is, and Luna silver we threpe,
Mars yren, Mercurie quik-silver we clepe,
Saturnus leed, and Jupiter is tin,
And Venus coper, by my fader kin !
   This cursed craft who-so wol exercyse,
He shal no good han that him may suffyse ;
For al the good he spendeth ther-aboute,
He lese shal, ther-of have I no doute.
Who-so that listeth outen his folye,
Lat him come forth, and lerne multiplye ;
And every man that oght hath in his cofre,
Lat him appere, and wexe a philosofre.
Ascaunce that craft is so light to lere ?
Nay, nay, god woot, al be he monk or frere,
Preest or chanoun, or any other wight,
Though he sitte at his book bothe day and night,
In lernyng of this elvish nyce lore,
Al is in veyn, and parde, mochel more !
To lerne a lewed man this subtiltee,
Fy ! spek nat ther-of, for it wol nat be ;
Al conne he letterure, or conne he noon,
As in effect, he shal finde it al oon.
For bothe two, by my savacioun,
Concluden, in multiplicacioun,
Y-lyke wel, whan they han al y-do ;
This is to seyn, they faylen bothe two.
   Yet forgat I to maken rehersaille
Of watres corosif and of limaille,
And of bodyes mollificacioun,

And also of hir induracioun,
Oiles, ablucions, and metal fusible,
To tellen al wolde passen any bible
That o-wher is ; wherfor, as for the beste,
Of alle thise names now wol I me reste.
For, as I trowe, I have yow told y-nowe
To reyse a feend, al loke he never so rowe.
  A! nay! lat be ; the philosophres stoon,
Elixir clept, we sechen faste echoon ;
For hadde we him, than were we siker y-now.
But, unto god of heven I make avow,
For al our craft, whan we han al y-do,
And al our sleighte, he wol nat come us to.
He hath y-maad us spenden mochel good,
For sorwe of which almost we wexen wood,
But that good hope crepeth in our herte,
Supposinge ever, though we sore smerte,
To be releved by him afterward ;
Swich supposing and hope is sharp and hard ;
I warne yow wel, it is to seken ever ;
That futur temps hath maad men to dissever,
In trust ther-of, from al that ever they hadde.
Yet of that art they can nat wexen sadde,
For unto hem it is a bitter swete ;
So semeth it ; for nadde they but a shete
Which that they mighte wrappe hem inne a-night,
And a bak to walken inne by day-light,
They wolde hem selle and spenden on this craft ;
They can nat stinte til no-thing be laft.
And evermore, wher that ever they goon,
Men may hem knowe by smel of brimstoon ;
For al the world, they stinken as a goot ;
Her savour is so rammish and so hoot,
That, though a man from hem a myle be,
The savour wol infecte him, trusteth me ;
Lo, thus by smelling and threedbare array,
If that men liste, this folk they knowe may.
And if a man wol aske hem prively,

Why they been clothed so unthriftily,
They right anon wol rownen in his ere,
And seyn, that if that they espyed were,
Men wolde hem slee, by-cause of hir science ;
Lo, thus this folk bitrayen innocence !

   Passe over this ; I go my tale un-to.
Er than the pot be on the fyr y-do,
Of metals with a certein quantitee,
My lord hem trempreth, and no man but he —
Now he is goon, I dar seyn boldely —
For, as men seyn, he can don craftily ;
Algate I woot wel he hath swich a name,
And yet ful ofte he renneth in a blame ;
And wite ye how ? ful ofte it happeth so,
The pot to-breketh, and farewel ! al is go !
Thise metals been of so greet violence,
Our walles mowe nat make hem resistence,
But if they weren wroght of lym and stoon ;
They percen so, and thurgh the wal they goon,
And somme of hem sinken in-to the ground —
Thus han we lost by tymes many a pound —
And somme are scatered al the floor aboute,
Somme lepe in-to the roof ; with-outen doute,
Though that the feend noght in our sighte him
      shewe,
I trowe he with us be, that ilke shrewe !
In helle wher that he is lord and sire,
Nis ther more wo, ne more rancour ne ire.
Whan that our pot is broke, as I have sayd,
Every man chit, and halt him yvel apayd.

   Som seyde, it was long on the fyr-making,
Som seyde, nay ! it was on the blowing ;
(Than was I fered, for that was myn office) ;
'Straw !' quod the thridde, 'ye been lewed and
      nyce,
It was nat tempred as it oghte be.'
'Nay !' quod the ferthe, 'stint, and herkne me ;
By-cause our fyr ne was nat maad of beech,

That is the cause, and other noon, so theech!'
I can nat telle wher-on it was long,
But wel I wot greet stryf is us among.

   'What!' quod my lord, 'ther is na-more to
      done,
Of thise perils I wol be war eft-sone ;
I am right siker that the pot was crased.
Be as be may, be ye no-thing amased ;
As usage is, lat swepe the floor as swythe,
Plukke up your hertes, and beth gladde and
      blythe.'

   The mullok on an hepe y-sweped was,
And on the floor y-cast a canevas,
And al this mullok in a sive y-throwe,
And sifted, and y-piked many a throwe.

   'Pardee,' quod oon, 'somwhat of our metal
Yet is ther heer, though that we han nat al.
Al-though this thing mishapped have as now,
Another tyme it may be wel y-now,
Us moste putte our good in aventure ;
A marchant, parde! may nat ay endure
Trusteth me wel, in his prosperitee ;
Somtyme his good is drenched in the see,
And somtym comth it sauf un-to the londe.'

   'Pees!' quod my lord, 'the next tyme I wol
      fonde
To bringe our craft al in another plyte ;
And but I do, sirs, lat me han the wyte ;
Ther was defaute in som-what, wel I woot.'

   Another seyde, the fyr was over hoot :—
But, be it hoot or cold, I dar seye this,
That we concluden evermore amis.
We fayle of that which that we wolden have,
And in our madnesse evermore we rave.
And whan we been togidres everichoon,
Every man semeth a Salomon.
But al thing which that shyneth as the gold
Nis nat gold, as that I have herd it told ;

Ne every appel that is fair at yë
Ne is nat good, what-so men clappe or crye.
Right so, lo ! fareth it amonges us ;
He that semeth the wysest, by Jesus !
Is most fool, whan it cometh to the preef ;
And he that semeth trewest is a theef ;
That shul ye knowe, er that I fro yow wende,
By that I of my tale have maad an ende.

GEOFFREY CHAUCER, *Canterbury Tales : Chanouns
Yemannes Tale*, Part 1 (*c.* 1398)

SCIENCE AND ORDER

THE heavens themselves, the planets, and this centre
Observe degree, priority, and place,
Insisture, course, proportion, season, form,
Office, and custom, in all line of order :
And therefore is the glorious planet Sol
In noble eminence enthron'd and spher'd
Amidst the other ; whose med'cinable eye
Corrects the ill aspects of planets evil,
And posts, like the commandment of a king,
Sans check, to good and bad : but when the planets
In evil mixture to disorder wander,
What plagues, and what portents, what mutiny,
What raging of the sea, shaking of earth.
Commotion in the winds, frights, changes, horrors,
Divert and crack, rend and deracinate
The unity and married calm of states
Quite from their fixure ! O ! when degree is shak'd,
Which is the ladder to all high designs,
The enterprise is sick.

From WILLIAM SHAKESPEARE, *Troilus and Cressida* (1602)

THE DISSOLUTION

SHEE's dead ; And all which die
   To their first Elements resolve ;
And wee were mutuall Elements to us,
    And made of one another.
   My body then doth hers involve,
And those things whereof I consist, hereby
In me abundant grow, and burdenous,
    And nourish not, but smother.
   My fire of Passion, sighes of ayre,
Water of teares, and earthly sad despaire,
      Which my materialls bee,
But neere worne out by loves securitie,
Shee, to my losse, doth by her death repaire,
    And I might live long wretched so
But that my fire doth with my fuell grow.
    Now as those Active Kings
   Whose foraine conquest treasure brings,
Receive more, and spend more, and soonest
    breake :
This (which I am amaz'd that I can speake)
    This death, hath with my store
      My use encreas'd.
And so my soule more earnestly releas'd,
Will outstrip hers ; As bullets flowen before
A latter bullet may o'rtake, the pouder being
    more.

                  JOHN DONNE, written *c.* 1598

NEW PHILOSOPHY

So did the world from the first houre decay,
That evening was beginning of the day,

And now the Springs and Sommers which we see,
Like sonnes of women after fiftie bee.
And new Philosophy calls all in doubt,
The Element of fire is quite put out ;
The Sun is lost, and th'earth, and no man's wit
Can well direct him where to looke for it.
And freely men confesse that this world's spent,
When in the Planets, and the Firmament
They seeke so many new ; then see that this
Is crumbled out againe to his Atomies.
'Tis all in peeces, all cohaerence gone ;
All just supply, and all Relation :
Prince, Subject, Father, Sonne, are things forgot,
For every man alone thinkes he hath got
To be a Phoenix, and that then can bee
None of that kinde, of which he is, but hee.
This is the worlds condition now, and now
She that should all parts to reunion bow,
She that had all Magnetique force alone,
To draw, and fasten sundred parts in one ;
She whom wise nature had invented then
When she observ'd that every sort of men
Did in their voyage in this worlds Sea stray,
And needed a new compasse for their way ;
She that was best, and first originall
Of all faire copies, and the generall
Steward to Fate ; she whose rich eyes, and breast
Guilt the West Indies, and perfum'd the East ;
Whose having breath'd in this world, did bestow
Spice on those Iles, and bad them still smell so,
And that rich Indie which doth gold interre,
Is but as single money, coyn'd from her :
She to whom this world must it selfe refer,
As Suburbs, or the Microcosme of her,
Shee, shee is dead ; shee's dead : when thou
    knowst this,
Thou knowst how lame a cripple this world is.
And learn'st thus much by our Anatomy,

That this worlds generall sickenesse doth not lie
In any humour, or one certaine part ;
But as thou sawest it rotten at the heart,
Thou seest a Hectique feaver hath got hold
Of the whole substance, not to be contrould,
And that thou hast but one way, not t'admit
The worlds infection, to be none of it.
For the worlds subtilst immateriall parts
Feele this consuming wound, and ages darts.
For the worlds beauty is decai'd, or gone,
Beauty, that's colour, and proportion.
We thinke the heavens enjoy their Sphericall,
Their round proportion embracing all.
But yet their various and perplexed course,
Observ'd in divers ages, doth enforce
Men to finde out so many Eccentrique parts,
Such divers downe-right lines, such overthwarts,
As disproportion that pure forme : It teares
The Firmament in eight and forty sheires,
And in these Constellations then arise
New starres, and old doe vanish from our eyes :
As though heav'n suffered earthquakes, peace or
    war,
When new Towers rise, and old demolish't are.
They have impal'd within a Zodiake
The free-borne Sun, and keepe twelve Signes awake
To watch his steps ; the Goat and Crab controule,
And fright him backe, who else to either Pole
(Did not these Tropiques fetter him) might runne :
For his course is not round ; nor can the Sunne
Perfit a Circle, or maintaine his way
One inch direct ; but where he rose to-day
He comes no more, but with a couzening line,
Steales by that point, and so is Serpentine :
And seeming weary with his reeling thus,
He meanes to sleepe, being now falne nearer us.
So, of the Starres which boast that they doe runne
In Circle still, none ends where he begun.

All their proportion's lame, it sinkes, it swels.
For of Meridians, and Parallels,
Man hath weav'd out a net, and this net throwne
Upon the Heavens, and now they are his owne.
Loth to goe up the hill, or labour thus
To goe to heaven, we make heaven come to us.
We spur, we reine the starres, and in their race
They're diversly content t'obey our pace.

From JOHN DONNE, *An Anatomie of the World :
The First Anniversary* (written 1611)

ALCHEMICAL THEORY OF GOLD

The Alchemist.   Ay, for 'twere absurd
To think that nature in the earth bred gold
Perfect in the instant : something went before.
There must be remote matter.
Surly.   Ay, what is that ?
The Alchemist.   It is, of the one part,
A humid exhalation, which we call
Materia liquida, or the unctuous water ;
On the other part, a certain crass and viscous
Portion of earth ; both which, concorporate,
Do make the elementary matter of gold ;
Which is not yet *propria materia*,
But common to all metals and all stones ;
For, where it is forsaken of that moisture,
And hath more dryness, it becomes a stone :
Where it retains more of the humid fatness,
It turns to sulphur, or to quicksilver,
Who are the parents of all other metals.
Nor can this remote matter suddenly
Progress so from extreme unto extreme,
As to grow gold, and leap o'er all the means.
Nature doth first beget the imperfect, then

26

Proceeds she to the perfect. Of that airy
And oily water, mercury is engender'd ;
Sulphur of the fat and earthy part ; the one,
Which is the last, supplying the place of male,
The other of the female, in all metals.
Some do believe hermaphrodeity,
That both do act and suffer. But these two
Make the rest ductile, malleable, extensive.
And even in gold they are ; for we do find
Seeds of them, by our fire, and gold in them ;
And can produce the species of each metal
More perfect thence, than nature doth in earth.
Beside, who doth not see in daily practice
Art can beget bees, hornets, beetles, wasps,
Out of the carcasses and dung of creatures ;
Yea, scorpions of an herb, being rightly placed ?
And these are living creatures, far more perfect
And excellent than metals.

From BEN JONSON, *The Alchemist* (1610)

VEINS, ARTERIES AND NERVES

NOR is there any part in all this land,
But is a little Isle : for thousand brooks
In azure channels glide on silver sand ;
Their serpent windings, and deceiving crooks
   Circling about, and wat'ring all the plain,
   Empty themselves into th'all-drinking main ;
And creeping forward slide, but never turn again.

Three diff'ring streams from fountains different,
Neither in nature nor in shape agreeing,
(Yet each with other friendly ever went)
Give to this Isle his fruitfulness and being :
   The first in single channels sky-like blue,

With luke-warm waters dyed in porphyr hue,
Sprinkle this crimson Isle with purple-colour'd dew.

The next, though from the same springs first it rise,
Yet passing through another greater fountain,
Doth lose his former name and qualities :
Through many a dale it flows, and many a mountain ;
  More fiery light, and needful more than all ;
  And therefore fenced with a double wall,
All froths his yellow streams with many a sudding fall.

The last, in all things diff'ring from the other,
Fall from an hill, and close together go,
Embracing as they run, each with his brother ;
Guarded with double trenches sure they flow :
  The coldest spring, yet nature best they have ;
  And like the lacteal stones which heaven pave,
Slide down to every part with their thick milky wave.

These with a thousand streams through th'Island roving,
Bring tribute in ; the first gives nourishment,
Next life, last sense and arbitrary moving :
For when the Prince hath now his mandate sent,
  The nimble posts quick down the river run,
  And end their journey, though but now begun ;
But now the mandate came, and now the mandate's done.

From PHINEAS FLETCHER, *The Purple Island,*
or *The Isle of Man* (1633)

A CENTRE FOR SCIENTIFIC RESEARCH

Argument

THE house of Astragon ; where in distress
Of Nature, Gondibert for Art's redress

Was by old Ulfin brought : where Art's hard strife,
In studying Nature for the aid of life,
Is by full wealth and conduct easy made ;
And Truth much visited, though in her shade.

He shows them now tow'rs of prodigious height,
  Where Nature's friends, philosophers remain
To censure meteors in their cause and flight,
  And watch the wind's authority on rain.

Others with optic tubes the Moon's scant face
  (Vast tubes, which like long cedars mounted lie)
Attract through glasses to so near a space,
  As if they came not to survey, but pry.

Nine hasty centuries are now fulfill'd,
  Since optics first were known to Astragon ;
By whom the moderns are become so skill'd,
  They dream of seeing to the maker's throne.

And wisely Astragon, thus busy grew,
  To seek the stars' remote societies ;
And judge the walks of th' old, by finding new ;
  For Nature's law in correspondence lies.

Man's pride (grown to religion) he abates,
  By moving our lov'd Earth ; which we think fix'd ;
Think all to it, and it to none relates ;
  With others' motion scorn to have it mix'd ;

As if 'twere great and stately to stand still
  Whilst other orbs dance on ; or else think all
Those vast bright globes (to show God's needless skill)
  Were made but to attend our little ball.

From Sir William Davenant, *Gondibert*, Book ii,
Canto V (1651)

PTOLEMY OR COPERNICUS?

THE ARGUMENT: *Adam inquires concerning celestial motions ; is doubtfully answered, and exhorted to search rather things more worthy of knowledge.*

THE Angel ended, and in Adam's ear
So charming left his voice that he a while
Thought him still speaking, still stood fixed to hear ;
Then, as new-waked, thus gratefully replied :—
  'What thanks sufficient, or what recompense
Equal, have I to render thee, divine
Historian, who thus largely hast allayed
The thirst I had of knowledge, and vouchsafed
This friendly condescension to relate
Things else by me unsearchable — now heard
With wonder, but delight, and, as is due,
With glory attributed to the high
Creator ? Something yet of doubt remains,
Which only thy solution can resolve.
When I behold this goodly frame, this World,
Of Heaven and Earth consisting, and compute
Their magnitudes — this Earth, a spot, a grain,
An atom, with the Firmament compared
And all her numbered stars, that seem to roll
Spaces incomprehensible (for such
Their distance argues, and their swift return
Diurnal) merely to officiate light
Round this opacous Earth, this punctual spot,
One day and night, in all their vast survey
Useless besides — reasoning, I oft admire
How Nature, wise and frugal, could commit
Such disproportions, with superfluous hand
So many nobler bodies to create,
Greater so manifold, to this one use,
For aught appears, and on their Orbs impose
Such restless revolution day by day

Repeated, while the sedentary Earth,
That better might with far less compass move,
Served by more noble than herself, attains
Her end without least motion, and receives,
As tribute, such a sumless journey brought
Of incorporeal speed, her warmth and light :
Speed, to describe whose swiftness number fails.'
  So spake our Sire, and by his countenance seemed
Entering on studious thoughts abstruse.

    .   .   .   .

And Raphael now to Adam's doubt proposed
Benevolent and facile thus replied :—
  'To ask or search I blame thee not ; for Heaven
Is as the Book of God before thee set,
Wherein to read his wondrous works, and learn
His seasons, hours, or days, or months, or years.
This to attain, whether Heaven move or Earth
Imports not, if thou reckon right ; the rest
From Man or Angel the great Architect
Did wisely to conceal, and not divulge
His secrets, to be scanned by them who ought
Rather admire.   Or, if they list to try
Conjecture, he his fabric of the Heavens
Hath left to their disputes — perhaps to move
His laughter at their quaint opinions wide
Hereafter, when they come to model Heaven,
And calculate the stars ; how they will wield
The mighty frame ; how build, unbuild, contrive
To save appearances ; how gird the Sphere
With Centric and Eccentric scribbled o'er,
Cycle and Epicycle, Orb in Orb.
Already by thy reasoning this I guess,
Who art to lead thy offspring, and supposest
That bodies bright and greater should not serve
The less not bright, nor Heaven such journeys run,
Earth sitting still, when she alone receives
The benefit. Consider, first, that great

Or bright infers not excellence. The Earth,
Though, in comparison of Heaven, so small,
Nor glistering, may of solid good contain
More plenty than the Sun that barren shines,
Whose virtue on itself works no effect,
But in the fruitful Earth ; there first received,
His beams, unactive else, their vigour find.
Yet not to Earth are those bright luminaries
Officious, but to thee, Earth's habitant.
And, for the Heaven's wide circuit, let it speak
The Maker's high magnificence, who built
So spacious, and his line stretched out so far,
That Man may know he dwells not in his own —
An edifice too large for him to fill,
Lodged in a small partition, and the rest
Ordained for uses to his Lord best known.
The swiftness of those Circles attribute,
Though numberless, to his omnipotence,
That to corporeal substances could add
Speed almost spiritual. Me thou think'st not slow,
Who since the morning-hour set out from Heaven
Where God resides, and ere mid-day arrived
In Eden — distance inexpressible
By numbers that have name. But this I urge,
Admitting motion in the Heavens, to show
Invalid that which thee to doubt it moved ;
Not that I so affirm, though so it seem
To thee who hast thy dwelling here on Earth.
God, to remove his ways from human sense,
Placed Heaven from Earth so far, that earthly sight,
And no advantage gain. What if the Sun
Be centre to the World, and other Stars,
By his attractive virtue and their own
Incited, dance about him various rounds ?
Their wandering course, now high, now low, then hid,
Progressive, retrograde, or standing still,
In six thou seest ; and what if, seventh to these,
The planet Earth, so steadfast though she seem,

Insensibly three different motions move ?
Which else to several spheres thou must ascribe,
Moved contrary with thwart obliquities,
Or save the Sun his labour, and that swift
Nocturnal and diurnal rhomb supposed,
Invisible else above all stars, the wheel
Of Day and Night ; which needs not thy belief,
If Earth, industrious of herself, fetch Day,
Travelling east, and with her part averse
From the Sun's beam meet Night, her other part
Still luminous by his ray. What if that light,
Sent from her through the wide transpicuous air,
To the terrestrial Moon be as a star,
Enlightening her by day, as she by night
This Earth — reciprocal, if land be there,
Fields and inhabitants ? Her spots thou seest
As clouds, and clouds may rain, and rain produce
Fruits in her softened soil, for some to eat
Allotted there ; and other Suns, perhaps,
With their attendant Moons, thou wilt descry,
Communicating male and female light —
Which two great sexes animate the World,
Stored in each Orb perhaps with some that live
For such vast room in Nature unpossessed
By living soul, desert and desolate,
Only to shine, yet scarce to contribute
Each Orb a glimpse of light, conveyed so far
Down to this habitable, which returns
Light back to them, is obvious to dispute.
But whether thus these things, or whether not —
Whether the Sun, predominant in heaven,
Rise on the Earth, or Earth rise on the Sun ;
He from the east his flaming road begin,
Or she from west her silent course advance
With inoffensive pace that spinning sleeps
On her soft axle, while she paces even,
And bears thee soft with the smooth air along —
Solicit not thy thoughts with matters hid :

Leave them to God above ; him serve and fear.
Of other creatures as him pleases best,
Wherever placed, let him dispose ; joy thou
In what he gives to thee, this Paradise
And thy fair Eve ; Heaven is for thee too high
To know what passes there. Be lowly wise ;
Think only what concerns thee and thy being ;
Dream not of other worlds, what creatures there
Live, in what state, condition, or degree —
Contented that thus far hath been revealed
Not of Earth only, but of Highest Heaven.'
    To whom thus Adam, cleared of doubt, replied :—
'How fully hast thou satisfied me, pure
Intelligence of Heaven, Angel serene,
And, freed from intricacies, taught to live
The easiest way, nor with perplexing thoughts
To interrupt the sweet of life, from which
God hath bid dwell far off all anxious cares,
And not molest us, unless we ourselves
Seek them with wandering thoughts, and notions vain !
But apt the mind or fancy is to rove
Unchecked ; and of her roving is no end,
Till, warned, or by experience taught, she learn
That not to know at large of things remote
From use, obscure and subtle, but to know
That which before us lies in daily life,
Is the prime wisdom ; what is more is fume,
Or emptiness, or fond impertinence,
And renders us in things that most concern
Unpractised, unprepared, and still to seek.

    From JOHN MILTON, *Paradise Lost*, Book VIII (1667)

HUDIBRAS — MATHEMATICIAN

IN mathematics he was greater
Than Tycho Brahe, or Erra Pater :

Samuel Butler

For he, by geometric scale,
Could take the size of pots of ale ;
Resolve, by sines and tangents straight,
If bread or butter wanted weight ;
And wisely tell what hour o' th' day
The clock does strike, by Algebra.

From SAMUEL BUTLER, *Hudibras*, Part 1 (1663)

ASTRONOMERS AND ASTROLOGERS

TH' Egyptians say, the sun has twice
Shifted his setting and his rise ;
Twice has he risen in the west,
As many times set in the east ;
But whether that be true or no,
The devil any of you know.
Some hold, the heavens, like a top,
Are kept by circulation up,
And were't not for their wheeling round,
They'd instantly fall to the ground ;
As sage Empedocles of old,
And from him modern authors hold.
Plato believed the sun and moon
Below all other planets run.
Some Mercury, some Venus seat
Above the Sun himself in height.
The learned Scaliger complained
'Gainst what Copernicus maintained,
That in twelve hundred years, and odd,
The Sun had left its ancient road,
And nearer to the Earth is come
'Bove fifty thousand miles from home ;
Swore 'twas a most notorious flam,
And he that had so little shame
To vent such fopperies abroad,

Deserved to have his rump well clawed ;
Which Monsieur Bodin hearing, swore
That he deserved the rod much more,
That durst upon a truth give doom,
He knew less than the pope of Rome.
Cardan believed great states depend
Upon the tip o' th' Bear's-tail's end ;
That as she whisked it towards the Sun,
Strowed mighty empires up and down ;
Which others say must needs be false,
Because your true bears have no tails.
Some say the Zodiac constellations
Have long since changed their antique stations
Above a sign, and prove the same
In Taurus now, once in the Ram ;
Affirmed the Trigons chopped and changed,
The watery with the fiery ranged ;
Then how can their effects still hold
To be the same they were of old ?
This, though the art were true, would make
Our modern soothsayers mistake,
And is one cause they tell more lies,
In figures and nativities,
Than th' old Chaldean conjurors,
In so many hundred thousand years.

From SAMUEL BUTLER, Hudibras, Part 2 (1664)

THE ELEPHANT IN THE MOON

A LEARNED society of late,
The glory of a foreign state,
Agreed, upon a summer's night,
To search the Moon by her own light ;
To make an inventory of all
Her real estate, and personal ;
And make an accurate survèy

Of all her lands, and how they lay,
As true as that of Ireland, where
The sly surveyors stole a shire :
T'observe her country, how 'twas planted,
With what sh' abounded most, or wanted ;
And make the proper'st observations
For settling of new plantations,
If the society should incline
T'attempt so glorious a design.

   This was the purpose of their meeting,
For which they chose a time as fitting ;
When at the full her radiant light
And influence too were at their height.
And now the lofty tube, the scale
With which they heaven itself assail,
Was mounted full against the Moon ;
And all stood ready to fall on,
Impatient who should have the honour
To plant an ensign first upon her.
When one, who for his deep belief
Was virtuoso then in chief,
Approved the most profound, and wise,
To solve impossibilities,
Advancing gravely, to apply
To th' optic glass his judging eye,
Cried, 'Strange !' — then reinforced his sight
Against the Moon with all his might,
And bent his penetrating brow,
As if he meant to gaze her through ;
When all the rest began t'admire,
And, like a train, from him took fire,
Surprised with wonder, beforehand,
At what they did not understand,
Cried out, impatient to know what
The matter was they wondered at.

   Quoth he, 'Th' inhabitants o' th' Moon,
Who, when the Sun shines hot at noon,
Do live in cellars under ground

Of eight miles deep, and eighty round,
In which at once they fortify
Against the sun and th' enemy,
Which they count towns and cities there,
Because their people's civiller
Than those rude peasants, that are found
To live upon the upper ground,
Called Privolvans, with whom they are
Perpetually in open war ;
And now both armies, highly enraged,
Are in a bloody fight engaged,
And many fall on both sides slain,
As by the glass 'tis clear, and plain.
Look quickly then, that every one
May see the fight before 'tis done.'

   With that a great philosopher,
Admired, and famous far and near,
As one of singular invention,
But universal comprehension,
Applied one eye, and half a nose
Unto the optic engine close.
For he had lately undertook
To prove, and publish in a book,
That men, whose natural eyes are out,
May, by more powerful art, be brought
To see with th' empty holes as plain,
As if their eyes were in again :
And, if they chanced to fail of those,
To make an optic of a nose ;
As clearly it may, by those that wear
But spectacles, be made appear ;
By which both senses being united,
Does render them much better sighted.
This great man, having fixed both sights
To view the formidable fights,
Observed his best, and then cried out, —
'The battle's desperately fought ;
The gallant Subvolvani rally,

And from their trenches make a sally
Upon the stubborn enemy,
Who now begin to rout and fly.
These silly ranting Privolvans,
Have every summer their campaigns,
And muster, like the warlike sons
Of Rawhead and of Bloodybones,
As numerous as Soland geese
I' th' islands of the Orcades,
Courageously to make a stand,
And face their neighbours hand to hand ;
Until the longed-for winter's come,
And then return in triumph home,
And spend the rest o' th' year in lies,
And vapouring of their victories.
From th' old Arcadians they're believed
To be, before the Moon, derived ;
And when her orb was new created,
To people her were thence translated.
For, as th' Arcadians were reputed
Of all the Grecians the most stupid,
Whom nothing in the world could bring
To civil life, but fiddleing,
They still retain the antique course,
And custom of their ancestors ;
And always sing, and fiddle to
Things of the greatest weight they do.'
   While thus the learned man entertains
Th' assembly with the Privolvans,
Another of as great renown,
And solid judgment in the Moon ;
That understood her various soils,
And which produced best genet-moyles ;
And in the register of fame
Had entered his long-living name ;
After he had pored long and hard
In th' engine, gave a start, and stared —
   Quoth he, 'A stranger sight appears

Than e'er was seen in all the spheres,
A wonder more unparalleled,
Than ever mortal tube beheld ;
An elephant from one of those
Two mighty armies is broke loose,
And with the horror of the fight
Appears amazed, and in a fright ;
Look quickly, lest the sight of us
Should cause the startled beast t' imboss.
It is a large one, far more great
Than e'er was bred in Afric yet ;
From which we boldly may infer,
The Moon is much the fruitfuller.
And, since the mighty Pyrrhus brought
Those living castles first, 'tis thought,
Against the Romans in the field,
It may an argument be held,
Arcadia being but a piece,
As his dominions were, of Greece,
To prove, what this illustrious person
Has made so noble a discourse on ;
And amply satisfied us all
Of th' Privolvans' original.
That elephants are in the Moon,
Though we had now discovered none,
Is easily made manifest,
Since, from the greatest to the least,
All other stars and constellations
Have cattle of all sorts of nations ;
And heaven, like a Tartar's horde,
With great and numerous droves is stored :
And, if the Moon produce by nature,
A people of so vast a stature,
'Tis consequent, she should bring forth
Far greater beasts too, than the earth,
As by the best accounts appears
Of all our great'st discoverers ;
And, that those monstrous creatures there

Are not such rarities as here.'
  Mean while the rest had had a sight
Of all particulars o' th' fight ;
And every man with equal care,
Perused of th' elephant his share,
Proud of his interest in the glory
Of so miraculous a story ;
When one, who for his excellence
In heightening words and shadowing sense,
And magnifying all he writ
With curious microscopic wit,
Was magnified himself no less
In home and foreign colleges,
Began, transported with the twang
Of his own trillo, thus t' harangue :
  'Most excellent and virtuous friends,
This great discovery makes amends
For all our unsuccessful pains,
And lost expense of time and brains.
For, by this sole phenomenon,
We 'ave gotten ground upon the Moon ;
And gained a pass, to hold dispute
With all the planets that stand out ;
To carry this most virtuous war
Home to the door of every star,
And plant th' artillery of our tubes
Against their proudest magnitudes ;
To stretch our victories beyond
Th' extent of planetary ground ;
And fix our engines, and our ensigns
Upon the fixed stars' vast dimensions, —
Which Archimede, so long ago,
Durst not presume to wish to do, —
And prove, if they are other suns,
As some have held opinions,
Or windows in the empyreum,
From whence those bright effluvias come
Like flames of fire, as others guess,

That shine i' the mouths of furnaces.
Nor is this all we have achieved,
But more, henceforth to be believed,
And have no more our best designs,
Because they're ours, believed ill signs.
T' out-throw, and stretch, and to enlarge,
Shall now no more be laid t'our charge ;
Nor shall our ablest virtuosos
Prove arguments for coffeehouses ;
Nor those devices, that are laid
Too truly on us, nor those made
Hereafter, gain belief among
Our strictest judges, right, or wrong ;
Nor shall our past misfortunes more
Be charged upon the ancient score ;
No more our making old dogs young
Make men suspect us still i' th' wrong ;
Nor new-invented chariots draw
The boys to course us, without law ;
Nor putting pigs t' a bitch to nurse,
To turn 'em into mongrel-curs,
Make them suspect our sculls are brittle,
And hold too much wit, or too little ;
Nor shall our speculations, whether
An elder-stick will save the leather
Of schoolboys' breeches from the rod,
Make all we do appear as odd.
This one discovery's enough,
To take all former scandals off.
But, since the world's incredulous
Of all our scrutinies, and us,
And with a prejudice prevents
Our best and worst experiments,
As if th' were destined to miscarry,
In consort tried, or solitary ;
And since it is uncertain when
Such wonders will occur again,
Let us as cautiously contrive

To draw an exact narrative
Of what we every one can swear
Our eyes themselves have seen appear,
That, when we publish the account,
We all may take our oaths upon 't.'
    This said, they all with one consent,
Agreed to draw up th' instrument,
And, for the general satisfaction,
To print it in the next 'Transaction'.
    But, whilst the chiefs were drawing up
This strange memoir o' th' telescope,
One, peeping in the tube by chance,
Beheld the elephant advance.
And, from the west side of the Moon
To th' east was in a moment gone.
This being related, gave a stop
To what the rest were drawing up ;
And every man, amazed anew
How it could possibly be true,
That any beast should run a race
So monstrous, in so short a space,
Resolved, howe'er, to make it good,
At least, as possible as he could ;
And rather his own eyes condemn,
Than question what h' had seen with them.
    While all were thus resolved, a man
Of great renown there, thus began —
    ''Tis strange, I grant ! But who can say
What cannot be ; what can, and may ?
Especially at so hugely vast
A distance, as this wonder's placed ;
Where the least error of the sight
May show things false, but never right ;
Nor can we try them, so far off,
By any sublunary proof.
For who can say, that nature there
Has the same laws she goes by here ?
Nor is it like, she has infused,

In every species, there produced,
The same efforts, she doth confer
Upon the same productions here :
Since those with us, of several nations,
Have such prodigious variations,
And she affects so much to use
Variety, in all she does.
Hence may b' inferred that, though I grant
We 've seen i' th' Moon an elephant,
That elephant may differ so
From those upon the earth below,
Both in his bulk, and force, and speed,
As being of a different breed ;
That, though our own are but slow-paced,
Theirs there may fly, or run as fast,
And yet be elephants no less,
Than those of Indian pedigrees.'
   This said, another of great worth,
Famed for his learnèd works, put forth,
Looked wise, then said — 'All this is true,
And learnedly observed by you ;
But there's another reason for't,
That falls but very little short
Of mathematic demonstration,
Upon an accurate calculation :
And that is — As the Earth and Moon
Do both move contrary upon
Their axes, the rapidity
Of both their motions cannot be
But so prodigiously fast,
That vaster spaces may be past
In less time than the beast has gone,
Though h' had no motion of his own ;
Which we can take no measure of,
As you have cleared by learnèd proof.
This granted, we may boldly thence
Lay claim to a nobler inference ;
And make this great phenomenon,

Were there no other, serve alone,
To clear the grand hypothesis
Of th' motion of the Earth from this.'
   With this they all were satisfied,
As men are wont o' th' biassed side ;
Applauded the profound dispute,
And grew more gay and resolute
By having overcome all doubt,
Than if it never had fall'n out ;
And, to complete their narrative,
Agreed t'insert this strange retrieve.
   But, while they were diverted all
With wording the memorial,
The footboys, for diversion too,
As having nothing else to do,
Seeing the telescope at leisure,
Turned virtuosos for their pleasure ;
Began to gaze upon the Moon,
As those they waited on, had done,
With monkeys' ingenuity,
That love to practise what they see ;
When one, whose turn it was to peep,
Saw something in the engine creep ;
And, viewing well, discovered more
Than all the learned had done before.
Quoth he, 'A little thing is slunk
Into the long star-gazing trunk ;
And now is gotten down so nigh,
I have him just against mine eye.'
   This being overheard by one,
Who was not so far overgrown
In any virtuous speculation,
To judge with mere imagination,
Immediately he made a guess
At solving all appearances,
A way far more significant,
Than all their hints of th' elephant,
And found, upon a second view,

His own hypothesis most true ;
For he had scarce applied his eye
To th' engine, but immediately
He found a mouse was gotten in
The hollow tube, and, shut between
The two glass windows in restraint
Was swelled into an elephant ;
And proved the virtuous occasion
Of all this learnèd dissertation :
And, as a mountain heretofore
Was great with child, they say, and bore
A silly mouse ; this mouse, as strange,
Brought forth a mountain, in exchange.

 Mean while, the rest in consultation
Had penned the wonderful narration ;
And set their hands, and seals, and wit,
T' attest the truth of what they writ ;
When this accursed phenomenon
Confounded all they'd said or done.
For 'twas no sooner hinted at,
But th' all were in a tumult straight,
More furiously enraged by far,
Than those that in the Moon made war,
To find so admirable a hint,
When they had all agreed t' have seen't,
And were engaged to make it out,
Obstructed with a paltry doubt.
When one, whose task was to determine,
And solve th' appearances of vermin ;
Who'd made profound discoveries
In frogs, and toads, and rats, and mice,
Though not so curious, 'tis true,
As many a wise rat-catcher knew,
After he had with signs made way
For something great he had to say,
 ——— 'This disquisition
Is, half of it, in my discission ;
For, though the elephant, as beast,

46

Belongs of right to all the rest,
The mouse, being but a vermin, none
Has title to, but I alone ;
And therefore hope, I may be heard,
In my own province, with regard.
It is no wonder we're cried down,
And made the talk of all the town,
That rants and swears, for all our great
Attempts, we have done nothing yet,
If every one have leave to doubt,
When some great secret's half made out ;
And, 'cause perhaps it is not true,
Obstruct, and ruin all we do.
As no great act was ever done,
Nor ever can, with truth alone ;
If nothing else but truth w' allow,
'Tis no great matter what we do.
For truth is too reserved, and nice,
T' appear in mixed societies ;
Delights in solit'ry abodes,
And never shows herself in crowds ;
A sullen little thing, below
All matters of pretence and show,
That deal in novelty, and change,
Not of things true, but rare and strange,
To treat the world with what is fit,
And proper to its natural wit ;
The world, that never sets esteem
On what things are, but what they seem ;
And if they be not strange and new
They're ne'er the better for being true.
For, what has mankind gained by knowing
His little truth, but his undoing,
Which wisely was by nature hidden,
And only for his good forbidden ?
And therefore, with great prudence does
The world still strive to keep it close ;
For, if all secret truths were known,

Who would not be once more undone ?
For truth has always danger in't,
And here, perhaps, may cross some hint,
We have already agreed upon,
And vainly frustrate all we've done,
Only to make new work for Stubbes,
And all the academic clubs.
How much then ought we have a care,
That no man know above his share ;
Nor dare to understand, henceforth,
More than his contribution's worth ;
That those who've purchased of the college
A share, or half a share of knowledge,
And brought in none, but spent repute,
Should not b'admitted to dispute,
Nor any man pretend to know
More than his dividend comes to ;
For partners have been always known
To cheat their public interest prone ;
And, if we do not look to ours,
'Tis sure to run the self-same course.'

    This said, the whole assembly allowed
The doctrine to be right and good ;
And, from the truth of what they'd heard,
Resolved to give truth no regard,
But what was for their turn, to vouch,
And either find, or make it such :
That 'twas more noble to create
Things like truth, out of strong conceit,
Than, with vexatious pains and doubt,
To find, or think t' have found her out.

    This being resolved, they, one by one,
Reviewed the tube, the mouse, and moon ;
But still, the narrower they pryed,
The more they were unsatisfied,
In no one thing, they saw, agreeing ;
As if they'd several faiths of seeing.
Some swore, upon a second view,

That all they'd seen before was true,
And that they never would recant
One syllable of th' elephant;
Avowed his snout could be no mouse's,
But a true elephant's proboscis.
Others began to doubt, and waver,
Uncertain which o' th' two to favour;
And knew not whether to espouse
The cause of th' elephant or mouse.
Some held no way so orthodox
To try it, as the ballot-box,
And, like the nation's patriots,
To find, or make, the truth by votes.
Others conceived it much more fit
T' unmount the tube, and open it;
And, for their private satisfaction,
To re-examine the 'Transaction',
And after explicate the rest,
As they should find cause for the best.
    To this, as th' only expedient,
The whole assembly gave consent;
But ere the tube was half let down,
It cleared the first phenomenon;
For, at the end, prodigious swarms
Of flies, and gnats, like men in arms,
Had all passed muster, by mischance,
Both for the Sub, and Privolvans.
This being discovered, put them all
Into a fresh, and fiercer brawl,
Ashamed, that men so grave and wise
Should be caldesed by gnats and flies,
And take the feeble insects' swarms
For mighty troops of men at arms;
As vain as those, who, when the Moon
Bright in a crystal river shone,
Threw casting-nets as subtly at her,
To catch and pull her out o' th' water.
But when they had unscrewed the glass,

To find out where th' impostor was,
And saw the mouse, that by mishap
Had made the telescope a trap,
Amazed, confounded, and afflicted,
To be so openly convicted,
Immediately they get them gone,
With this discovery alone :
That those who greedily pursue
Things wonderful, instead of true ;
That in their speculations choose
To make discoveries strange news ;
And natural history a gazette
Of tales stupendous, and far-fet ;
Hold no truth worthy to be known,
That is not huge and overgrown,
And explicate appearances,
Not as they are, but as they please,
In vain strive nature to suborn,
And, for their pains, are paid with scorn.

SAMUEL BUTLER, written *c.* 1676

ODE ON DR. HARVEY

I

COY Nature, (which remained, though aged grown,
A beauteous virgin still, enjoyed by none,
Nor seen unveiled by anyone)
When Harvey's violent passion she did see,
Began to tremble, and to flee,
Took sanctuary like Daphne in a tree :
There Daphne's lover stopped, and thought it much
The very leaves of her to touch,
But Harvey, our Apollo, stopped not so,
Into the bark and root he after her did go ;
No smallest fibres of a plant,

For which the eyebeam's point doth sharpness want,
His passage after her withstood.
What should she do ? Through all the moving wood
Of lives endowed with sense she took her flight,
Harvey pursues, and keeps her still in sight.
But, as the deer long-hunted takes a flood,
She leaped at last into the winding streams of blood ;
Of man's Meander all the purple reaches made,
Till at the heart she stayed,
Where turning head, and at a bay,
Thus, by well-purged ears, was she o'erheard to say.

2

Here sure shall I be safe (said she)
None will be able sure to see
This my retreat, but only He
Who made both it and me.
The heart of man, what art can e'er reveal ?
A wall impervious between
Divides the very parts within,
And doth the heart of man even from itself conceal.
She spoke, but e'er she was aware,
Harvey was with her there,
And held this slippery Proteus in a chain,
Till all her mighty mysteries she descried,
Which from his wit the attempt before to hide
Was the first thing that Nature did in vain.

3

He the young practice of new life did see,
Whilst to conceal its toilsome poverty,
It for a living wrought, both hard and privately.
Before the liver understood
The noble scarlet dye of blood,
Before one drop was by it made,
Or brought into it, to set up the trade ;
Before the untaught heart began to beat
The tuneful march to vital heat,

From all the souls that living buildings rear,
Whether implied for earth, or sea, or air,
Whether it in the womb or egg be wrought,
A strict account to him is hourly brought,
How the great fabric does proceed,
What time and what materials it does need.
He so exactly does the work survey,
As if he hired the workers by the day.

4

Thus Harvey sought for truth in truth's own book
The creatures, which by God himself was writ ;
And wisely thought 'twas fit,
Not to read comments only upon it,
But on the original itself to look.
Methinks in art's great circle others stand
Locked up together, hand in hand,
Everyone leads as he is led,
The same bare path they tread,
A dance like fairies a fantastic round,
But neither change their motion, nor their ground :
Had Harvey to this road confined his wit,
His noble circle of the blood had been untrodden yet.
Great doctor ! The art of curing's cured by thee,
We now thy patient Physic see,
From all inveterate diseases free,
Purged of old errors by thy care,
New dieted, put forth to clearer air,
It now will strong and healthful prove,
Itself before lethargic lay, and could not move.

5

These useful secrets to his pen we owe,
And thousands more 'twas ready to bestow ;
Of which a barbarous war's unlearned rage
Has robbed the ruined age ;
O cruel loss ! as if the Golden Fleece,
With so much cost and labour bought,

And from afar by a great hero brought
Had sunk even in the ports of Greece.
O cursed war ! Who can forgive thee this ?
Houses and towns may rise again,
And ten times easier it is
To rebuild Paul's, than any work of his.
That mighty task none but himself can do,
Nay, scarce himself too now,
For though his wit the force of age withstand,
His body, alas ! And Time it must command,
And Nature now, so long by him surpassed,
Will sure have her revenge on him at last.

ABRAHAM COWLEY, *Verses written on Several*
Occasions (1663)

TO THE ROYAL SOCIETY

I

PHILOSOPHY ! the great and only heir
Of all that human knowledge which has been
Unforfeited by man's rebellious sin,
Though full of years he do appear,
(Philosophy ! I say, and call it he,
For whatsoe'er the painter's fancy be,
It a male virtue seems to me)
Has still been kept in nonage till of late,
Nor managed or enjoyed his vast estate.
Three or four thousand years one would have thought,
To ripeness and perfection might have brought
A science so well bred and nursed,
And of such hopeful parts, too, at the first ;
But oh ! the guardians and the tutors then,
(Some negligent, and some ambitious men)
Would ne'er consent to set him free.
Or his own natural powers to let him see,
Lest that should put an end to their authority.

2

That his own business he might quite forget,
They amused him with the sports of wanton wit ;
With the desserts of poetry they fed him,
Instead of solid meats t'increase his force ;
Instead of vigorous exercise they led him
Into the pleasant labyrinths of ever-fresh discourse :
Instead of carrying him to see
The riches which do hoarded for him lie
In Nature's endless treasury,
They chose his eye to entertain
(His curious, but not covetous, eye)
With painted scenes and pageants of the brain.
Some few exalted spirits this latter age has shown,
That laboured to assert the liberty
(From guardians who were now usurpers grown)
Of this old minor still, captured Philosophy ;
But 'twas rebellion called, to fight
For such a long-oppressed right.
Bacon, at last, a mighty man, arose,
Whom a wise king and nature chose
Lord Chancellor of both their laws,
And boldly undertook the injured pupil's cause.

3

Authority, which did a body boast
Though 'twas but air condensed, and stalked about
Like some old giant's more gigantic ghost,
To terrify the learned rout,
With the plain magic of true reason's light
He chased out of our sight,
Nor suffered living men to be misled
By the vain shadows of the dead :
To graves, from whence it rose, the conquered
     phantom fled.
He broke that monstrous god which stood,
In midst of the orchard, and the whole did claim,

Which with a useless scythe of wood,
And something else not worth a name,
(Both vast for show, yet neither fit
Or to defend, or to beget ;
Ridiculous and senseless terrors !) made
Children and superstitious men afraid.
The orchard's open now, and free :
Bacon has broke that scarecrow Deity ;
Come, enter, all that will,
Behold the ripened Fruit, come gather now your fill.
Yet still, methinks, we fain would be
Catching at the forbidden tree ;
We would be like the Deity
When truth and falsehood, good and evil, we
Without the senses and within ourselves would see ;
For 'tis God only who can find
All nature in his mind.

4

From words, which are but pictures of the thought
(Though we our thoughts from them perversely
        drew),
To things, the mind's right object, he it brought ;
Like foolish birds to painted grapes we flew.
He sought and gathered for our use the true ;
And when on heaps the chosen bunches lay,
He pressed them wisely the mechanic way,
Till all their juice did in one vessel join,
Ferment into a nourishment divine
The thirsty soul's refreshing wine.
Who to the life an exact piece would make,
Must not from others' work a copy take ;
No, not from Rubens or Vandyck ;
Much less content himself to make it like
The ideas and the images which lie
In his own fancy or his memory :
No, he before his sight must place
The natural and living face ;

The real object must command
Each judgement of his eye, and motion of his hand.

5

From these, and all long errors of the way,
In which our wandering predecessors went,
And, like the old Hebrews, many years did stray,
In deserts, but of small extent,
Bacon, like Moses, led us forth at last ;
The barren wilderness he passed,
Did on the very border stand
Of the blessed Promised Land,
And from the mountain's top of his exalted wit,
Saw it himself, and showed us it.
But life did never to one man allow
Time to discover worlds and conquer too ;
Nor can so short a line sufficient be
To fathom the vast depths of Nature's sea :
The work he did we ought t'admire,
And were unjust if we should more require
From his few years, divided 'twixt excess
Of low affliction and high happiness :
For who on things remote can fix his sight,
That's always in a triumph or a fight ?

6

From you, great champions, we expect to get
These spacious countries but discovered yet ;
Countries where yet, instead of Nature, we
Her images and idols worshipped see :
These large and wealthy regions to subdue,
Though Learning has whole armies at command,
Quartered about in every land,
A better troop she ne'er together drew.
Methinks, like Gideon's little band,
God with design has picked out you,
To do these noble wonders by a few.
When the whole host He saw, they are, said He,

Too many to o'ercome for Me :
And now he chooses out his men,
Much in the way that He did then :
Not those many, whom He found
Idly extended on the ground,
To drink with their dejected head
The stream just so as by their mouths it fled :
No ; but those few who took the waters up,
And made of their laborious hands the cup.

7

Thus you prepared, and in the glorious fight
Their wondrous pattern too you take :
Their old and empty pitchers first they brake,
And with their hands then lifted up the light.
Iö ! sound too the trumpets here !
Already your victorious lights appear ;
New scenes of heaven already we espy,
And crowds of golden worlds on high,
Which from the spacious plains of earth and sea
Could never yet discovered be
By sailor's or Chaldean's watchful eye.
Nature's great works no distance can obscure,
No smallness her near objects can secure.
You have taught the curious sight to press
Into the privatest recess
Of her imperceptible littleness :
She with much stranger art than his who put
All the Iliads in a nut,
The numerous work of life does into atoms shut ;
You have learned to read her smallest hand,
And well begun her deepest sense to understand.

8

Mischief and true dishonour fall on those
Who would to laughter or to scorn expose
So virtuous and so noble a design,
So human for its use, for knowledge so divine.

The things which these proud men despise, and call
Impertinent, and vain, and small,
Those smallest things of nature let me know,
Rather than all their greatest actions do.
Whoever would desposed truth advance
Into the throne usurped from it,
Must feel at first the blows of ignorance,
And the sharp points of envious wit.
So when, by various turns of the celestial dance,
In many thousand years
A star, so long unknown, appears,
Though heaven itself more beauteous by it grow,
It troubles and alarms the world below,
Does to the wise a star, to fools a meteor, show.

9

With courage and success you the bold work begin;
Your cradle has not idle been;
None e'er but Hercules and you could be
At five years' age worthy a history;
And ne'er did fortune better yet
The historian to the story fit.
As you from all old errors free
And purge the body of Philosophy,
So from all modern follies he
Has vindicated eloquence and wit:
His candid style like a clean stream does slide,
And his bright fancy all the way
Does, like the sunshine, in it play;
It does like Thames, the best of rivers, glide,
Where the god does not rudely overturn,
But gently pour, the crystal urn,
And with judicious hand does the whole current
    guide.
'T has all the beauties Nature can impart,
And all the comely dress, without the paint, of Art.

ABRAHAM COWLEY, in Sprat's *History of the
Royal Society* (1667)

John Dryden

TO DR. CHARLETON

The longest tyranny that ever swayed
Was that wherein our ancestors betrayed
Their free-born reason to the Stagirite,
And made his torch their universal light.
So truth, while only one supplied the state,
Grew scarce and dear, and yet sophisticate ;
Until 'twas bought, like empiric wares or charms,
Hard words sealed up with Aristotle's arms.
Columbus was the first that shook his throne,
And found a temperate in a torrid zone,
The feverish air fanned by a cooling breeze,
The fruitful vales set round with shady trees,
And guiltless men, that danced away their time,
Fresh as their groves and happy as their clime.
Had we still paid that homage to a name
Which only God and Nature justly claim,
The western seas had been our utmost bound,
Where poets still might dream the sun was drowned,
And all the stars, that shine in southern skies,
Had been admired by none but savage eyes.
   Among the asserters of free reason's claim,
The English are not the least in worth or fame.
The world to Bacon does not only owe
Its present knowledge, but its future too.
Gilbert shall live, till loadstones cease to draw
Or British fleets the boundless ocean awe,
And noble Boyle, not less in nature seen,
Than his great brother, read in states and men.
The circling streams, once thought but pools, of blood
(Whether life's fuel or the body's food),
From dark oblivion Harvey's name shall save ;
While Ent keeps all the honour that he gave.
Nor are you, learned friend, the least renowned ;
Whose fame, not circumscribed with English ground,
Flies like the nimble journeys of the light,

And is, like that, unspent too in its flight.
Whatever truths have been by art or chance
Redeemed from error or from ignorance,
Thin in their authors, like rich veins in ore,
Your works unite, and still discover more.
Such is the healing virtue of your pen
To perfect cures on books as well as men.
Nor is this work the least : you well may give
To men new vigour, who make stones to live.
Through you the Danes, their short dominion lòst,
A longer conquest than the Saxons boast.
Stonehenge, once thought a temple, you have found
A throne where kings, our earthly gods, were crowned ;
Where by their wondering subjects they were seen,
Joyed with their stature and their princely mien.
Our Sovereign here above the rest might stand,
And here be chose again to sway the land.
    These ruins sheltered once his sacred head,
Then when from Worcester's fatal field he fled ;
Watched by the genius of this royal place,
And mighty visions of the Danish race,
His refuge then was for a temple shown :
But, he restored, 'tis now become a throne.

JOHN DRYDEN, written 1662

SHIPPING, NAVIGATION AND THE ROYAL SOCIETY

By viewing nature Nature's handmaid, Art,
    Makes mighty things from small beginnings grow :
Thus fishes first to shipping did impart
    Their tail the rudder and their head the prow.

Some log perhaps upon the waters swam,
    An useless drift, which, rudely cut within

And hollowed, first a floating trough became
  And cross some rivulet passage did begin.

In shipping such as this the Irish kern
  And untaught Indian on the stream did glide,
Ere sharp-keeled boats to stem the flood did learn,
  Or fin-like oars did spread from either side.

Add but a sail, and Saturn so appeared.
  When from lost empire he to exile went,
And with the golden age to Tiber steered,
  Where coin and first commerce he did invent.

Rude as their ships was navigation then,
  No useful compass or meridian known ;
Coasting, they kept the land within their ken,
  And knew no North but when the pole-star shone.

Of all who since have used the open sea
  Than the bold English none more fame have won ;
Beyond the year, and out of Heaven's high way,
  They make discoveries where they see no sun.

But what so long in vain, and yet unknown,
  By poor mankind's benighted wit is sought,
Shall in this age to Britain first be shown
  And hence be to admiring nations taught.

The ebbs of tides and their mysterious flow
  We, as arts' elements, shall understand,
And as by line upon the ocean go
  Whose paths shall be familiar as the land.

Instructed ships shall sail to quick commerce,
  By which remotest regions are allied ;
Which makes one city of the universe,
  Where some may gain and all may be supplied.

Then we upon our globe's last verge shall go
  And view the ocean leaning on the sky :
From thence our rolling neighbours we shall know
  And on the lunar world securely pry.

This I foretell, from your auspicious care
  Who great in search of God and Nature grow ;
Who best your wise Creator's praise declare,
  Since best to praise His works is best to know.

O, truly Royal ! who behold the law
  And rule of beings in your Maker's mind,
And thence, like limbecs, rich ideas draw
  To fit the levelled use of human kind.

From JOHN DRYDEN, *Annus Mirabilis*, 1666 (1667)

ANATOMY AND REVELATION

WHEN first the womb did the crude embryo hold,
What shap'd the parts ? What did the limbs unfold ?
O'er the whole work in secret did preside,
Give quick'ning vigour, and each motion guide ?
What kindled in the dark the vital flame,
And e'er the heart was form'd, push'd on the red'ning
    stream ?
Then for the heart the aptest fibres strung ?
And in the breast th' impulsive engine hung ?
Say, what the various bones so wisely wrought ?
How was their frame to such perfection brought ?
What did their figures for their uses fit,
Their number fix, and joints adapted knit ;
And made them all in that just order stand,
Which motion, strength and ornament demand ?
What for the sinews spun so strong a thread,
The curious loom to weave the muscles spread ?

Did the nice strings of tender membranes drill
And perforate the nerve with so much skill,
Then with the active stream the dark recesses fill ?
The purple mazes of the veins display'd,
And all th' arterial pipes in order laid,
What gave the bounding current to the blood,
And to and fro convey'd the restless flood ?
   The living fabric now in pieces take,
Of ev'ry part due observation make ;
All which such art discover, so conduce
To beauty, vigour, and each destin'd use ;
The atheist, if to search for truth inclin'd,
May in himself his full conviction find,
And from his body teach his erring mind.

   The salient point, so first is call'd the heart,
Shap'd and suspended with amazing art,
By turns dilated, and by turns comprest,
Expels, and entertains the purple guest.
It sends from out its left contracted side
Into th' arterial tube its vital pride :
Which tube, prolong'd but little from its source,
Parts its wide trunk, and takes a double course ;
One channel to the head its way directs,
One to th' inferior limbs its path inflects.
Both smaller by degrees, and smaller grow,
And on the parts, thro' which they branching go,
A thousand secret, subtle pipes bestow.
From which by num'rous convolutions wound,
Wrapt with th' attending nerve, and twisted round,
The complicated knots and kernels rise,
Of various figures, and of various size.
Th' arterial ducts, when thus involv'd, produce
Unnumber'd glands, and of important use.
But after, as they farther progress make,
The appellation of a vein they take.
For tho' th' arterial pipes themselves extend
In smallest branches, yet they never end :

The same continu'd circling channels run
Back to the heart, where first their course begun.

Thou, wondrous Harvey, whose immortal fame,
By thee instructed, grateful schools proclaim,
Thou, Albion's pride, didst first the winding way,
And circling life's dark labyrinth display.
Attentive from the heart thou didst pursue
The starting flood, and keep it still in view,
Till thou with rapture saw'st the channels bring
The purple currents back, and form the vital ring.

Thus has the Muse a daring wing display'd,
Thro' trackless skies ambitious flight essay'd,
To sing the wonders of the human frame.
Who can this field of miracles survey,
And not with Galen all in rapture say,
Behold a God, adore Him, and obey !

From SIR RICHARD BLACKMORE, *Creation*,
Book VI (1712)

THE COLLEGE OF PHYSICIANS

SPEAK, Goddess ! since 'tis thou that best canst tell,
How ancient leagues to modern discord fell ;
And why physicians were so cautious grown
Of others' lives, and lavish of their own ;
How by a journey to th' Elysian plain
Peace triumph'd, and old Time return'd again.
Not far from that most celebrated place,
Where angry Justice shows her awful face ;
Where little villains must submit to fate,
That great ones may enjoy the world in state ;
There stands a dome, majestic to the sight,
And sumptuous arches bear its oval height ;

A golden globe, plac'd high with artful skill,
Seems, to the distant sight, a gilded pill :
This pile was, by the pious patron's aim,
Rais'd for a use as noble as its frame ;
Nor did the learn'd society decline
The propagation of that great design ;
In all her mazes, Nature's face they view'd,
And, as she disappear'd, their search pursued.
Wrapt in the shade of night the goddess lies,
Yet to the learn'd unveils her dark disguise,
But shuns the gross access of vulgar eyes.

   Now she unfolds the faint and dawning strife
Of infant atoms kindling into life ;
How ductile matter new meanders takes,
And slender trains of twisting fibres makes ;
And how the viscous seeks a closer tone,
By just degrees to harden into bone ;
While the more loose flow from the vital urn,
And in full tides of purple streams return ;
How lambent flames from life's bright lamps arise,
And dart in emanations through the eyes ;
How from each sluice a gentle torrent pours,
To slake a feverish heat with ambient showers ;
Whence their mechanic powers the spirits claim ;
How great their force, how delicate their frame ;
How the same nerves are fashion'd to sustain
The greatest pleasure and the greatest pain ;
Why bilious juice a golden light puts on,
And floods of chyle in silver currents run ;
How the dim speck of entity began
T' extend its recent form, and stretch to man ;
To how minute an origin we owe
Young Ammon, Cæsar, and the great Nassau ;
Why paler looks impetuous rage proclaim,
And why chill virgins redden into flame ;
Why envy oft' transforms with wan disguise,
And why gay mirth sits smiling in the eyes ;
All ice why Lucrece ; or Sempronia, fire ;

Why Scarsdale rages to survive desire ;
When Milo's vigour at th' Olympic's shown,
Whence tropes to Finch, or impudence to Sloane ;
How matter, by the vary'd shape of pores,
Or idiots frames, or solemn senators.

Hence 'tis we wait the wondrous cause to find,
How body acts upon impassive mind ;
How fumes of wine the thinking part can fire,
Past hopes revive, and present joys inspire ;
Why our complexions oft our soul declare,
And how the passions in the feature are ;
How touch and harmony arise between
Corporeal figure, and a form unseen ;
How quick their faculties the limbs fulfil,
And act at every summons of the will ;
With mighty truths, mysterious to descry,
Which in the womb of distant causes lie.

But now no grand inquiries are descry'd,
Mean faction reigns where knowledge should preside,
Feuds are increas'd, and learning laid aside.
Thus synods oft concern for faith conceal,
And for important nothings show a zeal :
The drooping sciences neglected pine,
And Pæan's beams with fading lustre shine.
No readers here with hectic looks are found,
Nor eyes in rheum, through midnight-watching,
    drown'd ;
The lonely edifice in sweats complains
That nothing there but sullen silence reigns.

This place, so fit for undisturb'd repose,
The god of Sloth for his asylum chose,
Upon a couch of down in these abodes,
Supine with folded arms he thoughtless nods ;
Indulging dreams his godhead lull to ease,
With murmurs of soft rills, and whispering trees :
The poppy and each numbing plant dispense
Their drowsy virtue, and dull indolence ;
No passions interrupt his easy reign,

No problems puzzle his lethargic brain ;
But dark oblivion guards his peaceful bed,
And lazy fogs hang lingering o'er his head.

From SIR SAMUEL GARTH, *The Dispensary* (1699)

THE MIND

ALMA in verse ; in prose, the mind,
By Aristotle's pen defin'd,
Throughout the body squat or tall,
Is, *bona fide*, all in all.
And yet, slap dash, is all again
In every sinew, nerve and vein.
Runs here and there, like Hamlet's ghost ;
While everywhere she rules the roast.

This system, Richard, we are told,
The men of Oxford firmly hold.
The Cambridge wits, you know, deny
With *Ipse dixit* to comply.
They say (for in good truth they speak
With small respect of that old Greek)
That, putting all his words together,
'Tis three blue beans in one blue bladder.

ALMA, they strenuously maintain,
Sits cock-horse on her throne, the brain ;
And from that seat of thought dispenses
Her sov'reign pleasure to the senses.
Two optic nerves, they say, she ties,
Like spectacles, across the eyes ;
By which the spirits bring her word,
Whene'er the balls are fix'd, or stirr'd ;
How quick at park and play they strike ;
The Duke they court ; the toast they like ;

And at St. James's turn their grace
From former friends, now out of place.

Without these aids, to be more serious,
Her pow'r, they hold, had been precarious :
The eyes might have conspir'd her ruin ;
And she not known, what they were doing.
Foolish it had been, and unkind,
That they should see, and she be blind.

Wise Nature likewise, they suppose,
Has drawn two conduits down our nose :
Could ALMA else with judgment tell,
When cabbage stinks, or roses smell ?
Or who would ask for her opinion
Between an oyster, and an onion ?
For from most bodies, Dick, you know,
Some little bits ask leave to flow ;
And, as thro' these canals they roll,
Bring up a sample of the whole.
Like footmen running before coaches,
To tell the inn, what lord approaches.

By nerves about our palate plac'd,
She likewise judges of the taste.
Else (dismal thought !) our warlike men
Might drink thick port for fine champagne ;
And our ill-judging wives and daughters
Mistake small-beer for citron-waters.

Hence too, that she might better hear,
She sets a drum at either ear ;
And loud or gentle, harsh or sweet,
Are but th' Alarums which they beat.

Last, to enjoy her sense of feeling
(A thing she much delights to deal in)

A thousand little nerves she sends
Quite to our toes, and fingers' ends ;
And these in gratitude again
Return their spirits to the brain ;
In which their figure being printed
(As just before, I think, I hinted)
ALMA inform'd can try the case,
As she had been upon the place.

Thus, while the judge gives diff'rent journeys
To country counsel, and attornies ;
He on the bench in quiet sits,
Deciding, as they bring the writs.
The Pope thus prays and sleeps at Rome,
And very seldom stirs from home :
Yet sending forth his holy spies,
And having heard what they advise,
He rules the Church's best dominions ;
And sets men's faith by his opinions.

The scholars of the Stagyrite,
Who for the old opinion fight,
Would make their modern friends confess,
The diff'rence but from more to less.
The mind, say they, while you sustain
To hold her station in the brain ;
You grant, at least, she is extended :
Ergo the whole dispute is ended.
For, 'till tomorrow should you plead
From form and structure of the head ;
The mind as visibly is seen
Extended thro' the whole machine.
Why should all honour then be ta'en
From lower parts to load the brain ;
When other limbs we plainly see,
Each in his way, as brisk as he ?

FROM MATTHEW PRIOR, *Alma, or The Progress
of the Mind*, Canto 1 (1718)

SCIENTIFIC THEOLOGY,
OR RELIGIOUS NATURALISM

This gorgeous apparatus ! this display !
This ostentation of creative power !
This theatre ! — what eye can take it in ?
By what divine enchantment was it raised,
For minds of the first magnitude to launch
In endless speculation, and adore ?
One sun by day, by night ten thousand shine ;
And light us deep into the Deity ;
How boundless in magnificence and might !
O what a confluence of ethereal fires,
Form urns unnumber'd, down the steep of heaven,
Streams to a point, and centres in my sight !
Nor tarries there ; I feel it at my heart.
My heart, at once, it humbles, and exalts ;
Lays it in dust, and calls it to the skies.
Who sees it unexalted ? or unawed ?
Who sees it, and can stop at what is seen ?
Material offspring of Omnipotence !
Inanimate, all-animating birth !
Work worthy Him who made it ! worthy praise !
All praise ! praise more than human ! nor denied
Thy praise divine ! — But though man, drown'd in
        sleep,
Withholds his homage, not alone I wake ;
Bright legions swarm unseen, and sing, unheard
By mortal ear, the glorious Architect,
In this His universal temple hung
With lustres, with innumerable lights,
That shed religion on the soul ; at once,
The temple, and the preacher ! O how loud
It calls devotion ! genuine growth of Night !
    Devotion ! daughter of Astronomy !
An undevout astronomer is mad.
True ; all things speak a God ; but in the small,

Men trace out Him ; in great, He seizes man ;
Seizes, and elevates, and wraps, and fills
With new inquiries, 'mid associates new.

.   .   .   .   .

Who turns his eye on Nature's midnight face,
But must inquire — 'What hand behind the scene,
What arm almighty, put these wheeling globes
In motion, and wound up the vast machine ?
Who rounded in his palm these spacious orbs ?
Who bowl'd them flaming through the dark profound,
Numerous as glittering gems of morning dew,
Or sparks from populous cities in a blaze,
And set the bosom of old Night on fire ?
Peopled her desert, and made horror smile ? '
Or, if the military style delights thee
(For stars have fought their battles, leagued with man),
'Who marshals this bright host ? enrols their names ?
Appoints their posts, their marches, and returns,
Punctual, at stated periods ? who disbands
These veteran troops, their final duty done,
If e'er disbanded ? ' — He, whose potent word,
Like the loud trumpet, levied first their powers
In Night's inglorious empire, where they slept
In beds of darkness : arm'd them with fierce flames,
Arranged, and disciplined, and clothed in gold ;
And call'd them out of chaos to the field,
Where now they war with vice and unbelief.

.   .   .   .   .

Lorenzo ! this may seem harangue to thee ;
Such all is apt to seem, that thwarts our will.
And dost thou, then, demand a simple proof
Of this great master moral of the skies,
Unskill'd, or disinclined, to read it there ?
Since 'tis the basis, and all drops without it,
Take it, in one compact, unbroken chain.
Such proof insists on an attentive ear ;

'Twill not make one amid a mob of thoughts,
And, for thy notice, struggle with the world.
Retire ; — the world shut out ; — thy thoughts call
    home ; —
Imagination's airy wing repress ; —
Lock up thy senses ; — let no passion stir ; —
Wake all to Reason ; — let her reign alone ; —
Then, in thy soul's deep silence, and the depth
Of Nature's silence, midnight, thus inquire,
As I have done ; and shall inquire no more.
In nature's channel, thus the questions run :
   'What am I ? and from whence ? — I nothing know,
But that I am ; and, since I am, conclude
Something eternal : had there e'er been nought,
Nought still had been : eternal there must be. —
But what eternal ? — Why not human race ?
And Adam's ancestors without an end ? —
That's hard to be conceived ; since every link
Of that long-chain'd succession is so frail ;
Can every part depend, and not the whole ?
Yet grant it true ; new difficulties rise ;
I'm still quite out at sea ; nor see the shore.
Whence earth, and these bright orbs ? — eternal too ?
Grant matter was eternal ; still these orbs
Would want some other father ; — much design
Is seen in all their motions, all their makes ;
Design implies intelligence, and art ;
That can't be from themselves — or man ; that art
Man scarce can comprehend, could man bestow ?
And nothing greater yet allow'd than man. —
Who, motion, foreign to the smallest grain,
Shot through vast masses of enormous weight ?
Who bid brute matter's restive lump assume
Such various forms, and gave it wings to fly ?
Has matter innate motion ? then each atom,
Asserting its indisputable right
To dance, would form an universe of dust :
Has matter none ? Then whence these glorious forms

72

And boundless flights, from shapeless, and reposed ?
Has matter more than motion ? Has it thought,
Judgment, and genius ? Is it deeply learn'd
In mathematics ? Has it framed such laws,
Which but to guess, a Newton made immortal ? —
If so, how each sage atom laughs at me,
Who think a clod inferior to a man !
If art, to form ; and counsel, to conduct ;
And that with greater far than human skill ;
Resides not in each block ; — a Godhead reigns. —
Grant, then, invisible, eternal, Mind ;
That granted, all is solved. — But, granting that,
Draw I not o'er me a still darker cloud ?
Grant I not that which I can ne'er conceive ?
A being without origin, or end ! —
Hail, human liberty ! There is no God —
Yet, why ? On either scheme that knot subsists ;
Subsist it must, in God, or human race ;
If in the last, how many knots beside,
Indissoluble all ? — Why choose it there,
Where, chosen, still subsist ten thousand more ?
Reject it, where, that chosen, all the rest
Dispersed, leave reason's whole horizon clear ?
This is not reason's dictate ; Reason says,
Close with the side where one grain turns the scale ; —
What vast preponderance is here ! can reason
With louder voice exclaim — Believe a God ?
And reason heard, is the sole mark of man.
What things impossible must man think true,
On any other system ! and how strange
To disbelieve, through mere credulity !'
    If, in this chain, Lorenzo finds no flaw,
Let it for ever bind him to belief.
And where the link, in which a flaw he finds ?
And, if a God there is, that God how great !
How great that Power, whose providential care
Through these bright orbs' dark centres darts a ray !
Of nature universal threads the whole !

And hangs creation, like a precious gem,
Though little, on the footstool of his throne !

From EDWARD YOUNG, *The Complaint, or Night
Thoughts, Night Ninth* (1744)

THE GREAT CHAIN OF BEING

THE bliss of man (could pride that blessing find)
Is not to act or think beyond mankind ;
No pow'rs of body or of soul to share,
But what his nature and his state can bear.
Why has not man a microscopic eye ?
For this plain reason, man is not a fly.
Say what the use, were finer optics giv'n,
T' inspect a mite, not comprehend the heav'n ?
Or touch, if tremblingly alive all o'er,
To smart and agonize at ev'ry pore ?
Or quick effluvia darting through the brain,
Die of a rose in aromatic pain ?
If nature thundered in his op'ning ears,
And stunned him with the music of the spheres,
How would he wish that heav'n had left him still
The whisp'ring zephyr, and the purling rill ?
Who finds not Providence all good and wise,
Alike in what it gives, and what it denies ?
  Far as creation's ample range extends,
The scale of sensual, mental pow'rs ascends :
Mark how it mounts, to man's imperial race,
From the green myriads in the peopled grass :
What modes of sight betwixt each wide extreme,
The mole's dim curtain, and the lynx's beam :
Of smell, the headlong lioness between,
And hound sagacious on the tainted green :
Of hearing, from the life that fills the flood,
To that which warbles through the vernal wood :

The spider's touch, how exquisitely fine !
Feels at each thread, and lives along the line :
In the nice bee, what sense so subtly true
From pois'nous herbs extracts the healing dew ?
How instinct varies in the grov'ling swine,
Compared, half-reas'ning elephant, with thine !
'Twixt that, and reason, what a nice barrier,
For ever sep'rate, yet for ever near !
Remembrance and reflection how allied ;
What thin partitions sense from thought divide ;
And middle natures, how they long to join,
Yet never passed th' insuperable line !
Without this just gradation, could they be
Subjected, these to those, or all to thee ?
The pow'rs of all subdued by thee alone,
Is not thy reason all these pow'rs in one ?

   See, through this air, this ocean, and this earth,
All matter quick, and bursting into birth.
Above, how high, progressive life may go !
Around, how wide ! how deep extend below !
Vast chain of being ! which from God began,
Natures ethereal, human, angel, man,
Beast, bird, fish, insect, what no eye can see,
No glass can reach ; from infinite to thee,
From thee to nothing. On superior pow'rs
Were we to press, inferior might on ours :
Or in the full creation leave a void,
Where, one step broken, the great scale's destroyed :
From nature's chain whatever link you strike,
Tenth or ten thousandth, breaks the chain alike.

   And, if each system in gradation roll
Alike essential to th' amazing whole,
The least confusion but in one, not all
That system only, but the whole must fall.
Let earth unbalanced from her orbit fly,
Planets and suns run lawless through the sky ;
Let ruling angels from their spheres be hurled,
Being on being wrecked, and world on world ;

Heav'n's whole foundations to their centre nod,
And nature tremble to the throne of God.
All this dread order break — for whom? for thee?
Vile worm! — O madness! pride! impiety!

From ALEXANDER POPE, *Essay on Man*, Epistle I (1732)

MAN AND SCIENCE

KNOW, then, thyself, presume not God to scan;
The proper study of mankind is man.
Placed on this isthmus of a middle state,
A being darkly wise, and rudely great:
With too much knowledge for the sceptic side,
With too much weakness for the stoic's pride,
He hangs between; in doubt to act, or rest;
In doubt to deem himself a god, or beast;
In doubt his mind or body to prefer;
Born but to die, and reas'ning but to err;
Alike in ignorance, his reason such,
Whether he thinks too little, or too much:
Chaos of thought and passion, all confused;
Still by himself abused, or disabused;
Created half to rise, and half to fall;
Great lord of all things, yet a prey to all;
Sole judge of truth, in endless error hurled;
The glory, jest, and riddle of the world!
Go, wondrous creature! mount where science
        guides,
Go, measure earth, weigh air, and state the tides;
Instruct the planets in what orbs to run,
Correct old Time, and regulate the sun;
Go, soar with Plato to th' empyreal sphere,
To the first good, first perfect, and first fair;
Or tread the mazy round his foll'wers trod,
And quitting sense call imitating God;

As eastern priests in giddy circles run,
And turn their heads to imitate the sun.
Go, teach Eternal Wisdom how to rule —
Then drop into thyself, and be a fool !
    Superior beings, when of late they saw
A mortal man unfold all nature's law,
Admired such wisdom in an earthly shape
And showed a Newton as we show an ape.
    Could he, whose rules the rapid comet bind,
Describe or fix one movement of his mind ?
Who saw its fires here rise, and there descend,
Explain his own beginning, or his end ?
Alas, what wonder ! man's superior part
Unchecked may rise, and climb from art to art ;
But when his own great work is but begun,
What reason weaves, by passion is undone.
    Trace science, then, with modesty thy guide ;
First strip off all her equipage of pride ;
Deduct what is but vanity or dress,
Or learning's luxury, or idleness ;
Or tricks to show the stretch of human brain,
Mere curious pleasure, or ingenious pain ;
Expunge the whole, or lop th' excrescent parts
Of all our vices have created arts ;
Then see how little the remaining sum,
Which served the past, and must the times to come !

From ALEXANDER POPE, *Essay on Man*, Epistle II (1732)

EPITAPH INTENDED FOR SIR ISAAC NEWTON IN WESTMINSTER ABBEY

NATURE and Nature's laws lay hid in night :
God said, 'Let Newton be !' and all was light.

ALEXANDER POPE, written 1732

TO THE MEMORY OF SIR ISAAC NEWTON

SHALL the great soul of Newton quit this earth,
To mingle with his stars ; and every Muse,
Astonished into silence, shun the weight
Of honours due to his illustrious name ?
But what can man ? — E'en now the sons of light,
In strains high warbled to seraphic lyre,
Hail his arrival on the coast of bliss.
Yet am not I deterred, though high the theme,
And sung to harps of angels, for with you,
Ethereal flames ! ambitious, I aspire
In Nature's general symphony to join.

And what new wonders can ye show your guest !
Who, while on this dim spot, where mortals toil
Clouded in dust, from Motion's simple laws,
Could trace the secret hand of Providence,
Wide-working through this universal frame.

Have ye not listened while he bound the suns
And planets to their spheres ! the unequal task
Of humankind till then. Oft had they rolled
O'er erring man the year, and oft disgraced
The pride of schools, before their course was known
Full in its causes and effects to him,
All-piercing sage ! Who sat not down and dreamed
Romantic schemes, defended by the din
Of specious words, and tyranny of names ;
But, bidding his amazing mind attend,
And with heroic patience years on years
Deep-searching, saw at last the system dawn,
And shine, of all his race, on him alone.

What were his raptures then ! how pure ! how
strong !
And what the triumphs of old Greece and Rome,
By his diminished, but the pride of boys
In some small fray victorious ! when instead
Of shattered parcels of this earth usurped

By violence unmanly, and sore deeds
Of cruelty and blood, Nature herself
Stood all subdued by him, and open laid
Her every latent glory to his view.
  All intellectual eye, our solar round
First gazing through, he by the blended power
Of gravitation and projection saw
The whole in silent harmony revolve.
From unassisted vision hid, the moons
To cheer remoter planets numerous formed,
By him in all their mingled tracts were seen.
He also fixed our wandering Queen of Night,
Whether she wanes into a scanty orb,
Or, waxing broad, with her pale shadowy light,
In a soft deluge overflows the sky.
Her every motion clear-discerning, he
Adjusted to the mutual main, and taught
Why now the mighty mass of water swells
Resistless, heaving on the broken rocks,
And the full river turning : till again
The tide revertive, unattracted, leaves
A yellow waste of idle sands behind.
  Then breaking hence, he took his ardent flight
Through the blue infinite ; and every star
Which the clear concave of a winter's night
Pours on the eye, or astronomic tube,
Far stretching, snatches from the dark abyss ;
Or such as further in successive skies
To fancy shine alone, at his approach
Blazed into suns, the living centre each
Of an harmonious system : all combined,
And ruled unerring by that single power,
Which draws the stone projected to the ground.
  O unprofuse magnificence divine !
O wisdom truly perfect ! thus to call
From a few causes such a scheme of things ;
Effects so various, beautiful, and great,
A universe complete ! And O, beloved

Of Heaven ! whose well purged penetrative eye
The mystic veil transpiercing, inly scanned
The rising, moving, wide-established frame.

He, first of men, with awful wing pursued
The Comet through the long elliptic curve,
As round innumerous worlds he wound his way ;
Till, to the forehead of our evening sky
Returned, the blazing wonder glares anew,
And o'er the trembling nations shakes dismay.

The heavens are all his own ; from the wild rule
Of whirling Vortices, and circling Spheres,
To their first great simplicity restored.
The schools astonished stood ; but found it vain
To combat still with demonstration strong,
And, unawakened, dream beneath the blaze
Of truth. At once their pleasing visions fled,
With the gay shadows of the morning mixed,
When Newton rose, our philosophic sun !

The aërial flow of Sound was known to him,
From whence it first in wavy circles breaks,
Till the touched organ takes the message in.
Nor could the darting beam of speed immense
Escape his swift pursuit, and measuring eye.
E'en Light itself, which every thing displays,
Shone undiscovered, till his brighter mind
Untwisted all the shining robe of day ;
And, from the whitening undistinguished blaze,
Collecting every ray into his kind,
To the charmed eye educed the gorgeous train
Of parent colours. First the flaming Red
Sprung vivid forth ; the tawny Orange next ;
And next delicious Yellow ; by whose side
Fell the kind beams of all-refreshing Green ;
Then the pure Blue, that swells autumnal skies,
Ethereal played ; and then, of sadder hue,
Emerged the deepened Indigo, as when
The heavy-skirted evening droops with frost ;
While the last gleamings of refracted light

Died in the fainting Violet away.
These, when the clouds distil the rosy shower,
Shine out distinct adown the watery bow ;
While o'er our heads the dewy vision bends
Delightful, melting on the fields beneath.
Myriads of mingling dyes from these result,
And myriads still remain ; infinite source
Of beauty, ever blushing, ever new.

   Did ever poet image aught so fair,
Dreaming in whispering groves, by the hoarse brook ;
Or prophet, to whose rapture heaven descends ?
E'en now the setting sun and shifting clouds,
Seen, Greenwich, from thy lovely heights, declare
How just, how beauteous the refractive law.

   The noiseless tide of Time, all bearing down
To vast eternity's unbounded sea,
Where the green islands of the happy shine,
He stemmed alone ; and to the source (involved
Deep in primeval gloom) ascending, raised
His lights at equal distances, to guide
Historian, wildered on his darksome way.

   But who can number up his labours ? who
His high discoveries sing ? when but a few
Of the deep-studying race can stretch their minds
To what he knew — in fancy's lighter thought,
How shall the muse then grasp the mighty theme ?

   What wonder thence that his devotion swelled
Responsive to his knowledge ? For could he,
Whose piercing mental eye diffusive saw
The finished university of things,
In all its order, magnitude, and parts,
Forbear incessant to adore that Power
Who fills, sustains, and actuates the whole ?

   Say, ye who best can tell, ye happy few,
Who saw him in the softest lights of life,
All unwithheld, indulging to his friends
The vast unborrowed treasures of his mind,
Oh, speak the wondrous man ! how mild, how calm,

How greatly humble, how divinely good ;
How firm established on eternal truth ;
Fervent in doing well, with every nerve
Still pressing on, forgetful of the past,
And panting for perfection : far above
Those little cares, and visionary joys,
That so perplex the fond impassioned heart
Of ever cheated, ever trusting man.

   And you, ye hopeless gloomy-minded tribe,
You who, unconscious of those nobler flights
That reach impatient at immortal life,
Against the prime endearing privilege
Of Being dare contend, — say, can a soul
Of such extensive, deep, tremendous powers,
Enlarging still, be but a finer breath
Of spirits dancing through their tubes awhile,
And then for ever lost in vacant air ?

   But hark ! methinks I hear a warning voice,
Solemn as when some awful change is come,
Sound through the world — ' 'Tis done ! — The
       measure's full ;
And I resign my charge.' — Ye mouldering stones,
That build the towering pyramid, the proud
Triumphal arch, the monument effaced
By ruthless ruin, and whate'er supports
The worshipped name of hoar antiquity,
Down to the dust ! What grandeur can ye boast
While Newton lifts his column to the skies,
Beyond the waste of time. Let no weak drop
Be shed for him. The virgin in her bloom
Cut off, the joyous youth, and darling child,
These are the tombs that claim the tender tear,
And elegiac song. But Newton calls
For other notes of gratulation high,
That now he wanders through those endless worlds
He here so well descried, and wondering talks,
And hymns their Author with his glad compeers.
O Britain's boast ! whether with angels thou

Sittest in dread discourse, or fellow-blessed,
Who joy to see the honour of their kind ;
Or whether, mounted on cherubic wing,
Thy swift career is with the whirling orbs,
Comparing things with things, in rapture lost,
And grateful adoration, for that light
So plenteous rayed into thy mind below,
From Light himself ; oh, look with pity down
On humankind, a frail erroneous race !
Exalt the spirit of a downward world !
O'er thy dejected Country chief preside,
And be her Genius called ! her studies raise,
Correct her manners, and inspire her youth.
For, though depraved and sunk, she brought thee
       forth,
And glories in thy name ; she points thee out
To all her sons, and bids them eye thy star :
While in expectance of the second life,
When time shall be no more, thy sacred dust
Sleeps with her kings, and dignifies the scene.

JAMES THOMSON, written 1727

THE VIRTUOSO

(In imitation of Spenser's style and stanza)

WHILOM by silver Thames's gentle stream,
In London town there dwelt a subtile wight ;
A wight of mickle wealth, and mickle fame,
Book-learned and quaint ; a Virtuoso hight.
Uncommon things, and rare, were his delight ;
From musings deep his brain ne'er gotten ease,
Nor ceasen he from study, day or night ;
Until (advancing onward by degrees)
He knew whatever breeds on earth, or air, or seas.

He many a creature did anatomize,
Almost unpeopling water, air, and land ;
Beasts, fishes, birds, snails, caterpillars, flies,
Were laid full low by his relentless hand,
That oft with gory crimson was distained :
He many a dog destroyed, and many a cat ;
Of fleas his bed, of frogs the marshes drained,
Could tellen if a mite were lean or fat,
And read a lecture o'er the entrails of a gnat.

He knew the various modes of ancient times,
Their arts and fashions of each different guise,
Their weddings, funerals, punishments for crimes,
Their strength, their learning eke, and rarities,
Of old habiliments, each sort and size,
Male, female, high and low, to him were known ;
Each gladiator-dress, and stage disguise ;
With learned, clerkly phrase he could have shown
How the Greek tunic differed from the Roman gown.

A curious medallist, I wot, he was,
And boasted many a course of ancient coin ;
Well as his wife's he knewen every face,
From Julius Cæsar down to Constantine :
For some rare sculptor he would oft ypine,
(As green-sick damosels for husbands do ;)
And when obtained, with enraptured eyne,
He'd run it o'er and o'er with greedy view,
And look, and look again, as he would look it through.

His rich museum, of dimensions fair,
With goods that spoke the owner's mind was fraught :
Things ancient, curious, value-worth, and rare,
From sea and land, from Greece and Rome were brought,
Which he with mighty sums of gold had bought :
On these all tides with joyous eyes he pored ;
And, sooth to say, himself he greater thought,
When he beheld his cabinets thus stored,
Than if he'd been of Albion's wealthy cities lord.

Here, in a corner, stood a rich scrutoire,
With many a curiosity replete ;
In seemly order furnished every drawer,
Products of art or nature as was meet ;
Air-pumps and prisms were placed beneath his feet,
A Memphian mummy-king hung o'er his head ;
Here phials with live insects small and great,
There stood a tripod of the Pythian maid ;
Above, a crocodile diffused a grateful shade.

Fast by the window did a table stand,
Where hodiern and antique rarities,
From Egypt, Greece, and Rome, from sea and land,
Were thick-besprent of every sort and size :
Here a Bahaman-spider's carcass lies,
There a dire serpent's golden skin doth shine ;
Here Indian feathers, fruits, and glittering flies ;
There gums and amber found beneath the line,
The beak of Ibis here, and there an Antonine.

Close at his back, or whispering in his ear,
There stood a spright ycleped Phantasy ;
Which, wheresoe'er he went, was always near :
Her look was wild, and roving was her eye ;
Her hair was clad with flowers of every dye ;
Her glistering robes were of more various hue,
Than the fair bow that paints the cloudy sky,
Or all the spangled drops of morning dew ;
Their colour changing still at every different view.

Yet in this shape all tides she did not stay,
Various as the chameleon that she bore ;
Now a grand monarch with a crown of hay,
Now mendicant in silks and golden ore :
A statesman now, equipped to chase the boar,
Or cowled monk, lean, feeble, and unfed ;
A clown-like lord, or swain of courtly lore
Now scribbling dunce in sacred laurel clad,
Or papal father now, in homely weeds arrayed.

The wight whose brain this phantom's power doth fill,
On whom she doth with constant care attend,
Will for a dreadful giant take a mill,
Or a grand palace in a hog-sty find :
(From her dire influence me may Heaven defend !)
All things with vitiated sight he spies ;
Neglects his family, forgets his friend,
Seeks painted trifles and fantastic toys,
And eagerly pursues imaginary joys.

MARK AKENSIDE, written 1737

HYMN TO SCIENCE

SCIENCE ! thou fair effusive ray
From the great source of mental day,
   Free, generous, and refined !
Descend with all thy treasures fraught,
Illumine each bewildered thought,
   And bless my labouring mind.

But first with thy resistless light
Disperse those phantoms from my sight,
   Those mimic shades of thee :
The scholiast's learning, sophist's cant,
The visionary bigot's rant,
   The monk's philosophy.

Oh ! let thy powerful charms impart
The patient head, the candid heart,
   Devoted to thy sway ;
Which no weak passions e'er mislead,
Which still with dauntless steps proceed
   Where reason points the way.

Give me to learn each secret cause ;
Let number's, figure's, motion's laws
   Revealed before me stand ;
These to great Nature's scenes apply,
And round the globe, and through the sky,
   Disclose her working hand.

Next, to thy nobler search resigned,
The busy, restless, human mind
   Through every maze pursue ;
Detect perception where it lies,
Catch the ideas as they rise,
   And all their changes view.

Say from what simple springs began
The vast ambitious thoughts of man,
   Which range beyond control,
Which seek eternity to trace,
Dive through the infinity of space,
   And strain to grasp the whole.

Her secret stores let memory tell,
Bid Fancy quit her fairy cell,
   In all her colours drest ;
While, prompt her sallies to control,
Reason, the judge, recalls the soul
   To Truth's severest test.

Then launch through being's wide extent ;
Let the fair scale with just ascent
   And cautious steps be trod ;
And from the dead, corporeal mass,
Through each progressive order, pass
   To Instinct, Reason, God.

There, Science, veil thy daring eye ;
Nor dive too deep, nor soar too high,
   In that divine abyss ;

To faith content thy beams to lend,
Her hopes t'assure, her steps befriend
   And light her way to bliss.

Then downwards take thy flight again,
Mix with the policies of men,
   And social nature's ties ;
The plan, the genius of each state,
Its interest and its powers relate,
   Its fortunes and its rise.

Through private life pursue thy course,
Trace every action to its source,
   And means and motives weigh :
Put tempers, passions, in the scale ;
Mark what degrees in each prevail,
   And fix the doubtful sway.

That last best effort of thy skill,
To form the life, and rule the will,
   Propitious power ! impart :
Teach me to cool my passion's fires,
Make me the judge of my desires,
   The master of my heart.

Raise me above the vulgar's breath,
Pursuit of fortune, fear of death,
   And all in life that's mean :
Still true to reason be my plan,
Still let my actions speak the man,
   Through every various scene.

Hail ! queen of manners, light of truth ;
Hail ! charm of age, and guide of youth ;
   Sweet refuge of distress :

In business, thou, exact, polite ;
Thou giv'st retirement its delight,
  Prosperity its grace.

Of wealth, power, freedom, thou the cause ;
Foundress of order, cities, laws ;
  Of arts inventress thou :
Without thee, what were human-kind ?
How vast their wants, their thoughts how
    blind !
  Their joys how mean, how few !

Sun of the soul ! thy beams unveil :
Let others spread the daring sail,
  On Fortune's faithless sea :
While, undeluded, happier I
From the vain tumult timely fly,
  And sit in peace with thee.

                    MARK AKENSIDE, written 1739

THE LOGICIANS REFUTED

(*Parody — Jonathan Swift*)

LOGICIANS have but ill defined
As rational the human mind ;
Reason, they say, belongs to man,
But let them prove it if they can.
Wise Aristotle and Smiglecius,
By ratiocinations specious,
Have strove to prove with great precision,
With definition and division,
Homo est ratione præditum ;
But for my soul I cannot credit 'em.
And must in spite of them maintain,

That man and all his ways are vain ;
And that this boasted lord of nature
Is both a weak and erring creature.
That instinct is a surer guide
Than reason — boasting mortal's pride ;
And that brute beasts are far before 'em,
Deus est anima brutorum.
Who ever knew an honest brute
At law his neighbour prosecute,
Bring action for assault and battery,
Or friend beguile with lies and flattery ?
O'er plains they ramble unconfined,
No politics disturb their mind ;
They eat their meals, and take their sport,
Nor know who's in or out at court,
They never to the levee go
To treat as dearest friend, a foe :
They never importune his Grace,
Nor ever cringe to men in place ;
Nor undertake a dirty job,
Nor draw the quill to write for Bob,
Fraught with invective they ne'er go,
To folks at Paternoster Row :
No judges, fiddlers, dancing-masters,
No pickpockets, or poetasters,
Are known to honest quadrupeds,
No single brute his fellow leads.
Brutes never meet in bloody fray,
Nor cut each others' throats for pay.
Of beasts, it is confessed, the ape
Comes nearest us in human shape,
Like man he imitates each fashion,
And malice is his ruling passion :
But both in malice and grimaces
A courtier any ape surpasses.
Behold him humbly cringing wait
Upon a minister of state :
View him soon after to inferiors,

Aping the conduct of superiors :
He promises with equal air,
And to perform takes equal care.
He in his turn finds imitators ;
At court, the porters, lacqueys, waiters,
Their masters' manners still contract,
And footmen, lords and dukes can act.
Thus at the court both great and small
Behave alike — for all ape all.

OLIVER GOLDSMITH, written 1759

SCIENCE AND THE TRUE KNOWLEDGE
OF GOD

I WAS a stricken deer, that left the herd
Long since. With many an arrow deep infix'd
My panting side was charg'd, when I withdrew,
To seek a tranquil death in distant shades.
There was I found by one, who had himself
Been hurt by th' archers. In his side he bore,
And in his hands and feet, the cruel scars.
With gentle force soliciting the darts,
He drew them forth, and heal'd, and bade me live.
Since then, with few associates, in remote
And silent woods I wander, far from those
My former partners of the peopled scene ;
With few associates, and not wishing more.
Here much I ruminate, as much I may,
With other views of men and manners now
Than once, and others of a life to come.
I see that all are wand'rers, gone astray
Each in his own delusions ; they are lost
In chase of fancied happiness, still woo'd
And never won. Dream after dream ensues ;

And still they dream, that they shall still succeed,
And still are disappointed. Rings the world
With the vain stir. I sum up half mankind,
And add two thirds of the remaining half,
And find the total of their hopes and fears
Dreams, empty dreams. The million flit as gay,
As if created only like the fly,
That spreads his motley wings in th' eye of noon,
To sport their season, and be seen no more.
The rest are sober dreamers, grave and wise,
And pregnant with discov'ries new and rare.
Some write a narrative of wars, and feats
Of heroes little known ; and call the rant
A history : describe the man, of whom
His own coevals took but little note,
And paint his person, character, and views,
As they had known him from his mother's womb.
They disentangle from the puzzled skein,
In which obscurity has wrapp'd them up,
The threads of politic and shrewd design,
That run through all his purposes, and charge
His mind with meanings that he never had,
Or, having, kept conceal'd. Some drill and bore
The solid earth, and from the strata there
Extract a register, by which we learn,
That he who made it, and reveal'd its date
To Moses, was mistaken in its age.
Some, more acute, and more industrious still,
Contrive creation ; travel nature up
To the sharp peak of her sublimest height,
And tell us whence the stars ; why some are fix'd,
And planetary some ; what gave them first
Rotation, from what fountain flow'd their light.
Great contest follows, and much learned dust
Involves the combatants ; each claiming truth,
And truth disclaiming both. And thus they spend
The little wick of life's poor shallow lamp
In playing tricks with nature, giving laws

To distant worlds, and trifling in their own.
Is't not a pity now, that tickling rheums
Should ever tease the lungs, and blear the sight
Of oracles like these ? Great pity too,
That having wielded th' elements, and built
A thousand systems, each in his own way,
They should go out in fume, and be forgot ?
Ah ! what is life thus spent ? and what are they
But frantic, who thus spend it ? all for smoke —
Eternity for bubbles proves at last
A senseless bargain. When I see such games
Play'd by the creatures of a pow'r, who swears
That he will judge the Earth, and call the fool
To a sharp reck'ning that has liv'd in vain ;
And when I weigh this seeming wisdom well,
And prove it in th'infallible result
So hollow and so false — I feel my heart
Dissolve in pity, and account the learn'd,
If this be learning, most of all deceiv'd.
Great crimes alarm the conscience, but it sleeps,
While thoughtful man is plausibly amus'd.
Defend me therefore, common sense, say I,
From reveries so airy, from the toil
Of dropping buckets into empty wells,
And growing old in drawing nothing up !

'Twere well, says one sage erudite, profound,
Terribly arch'd, and aquiline his nose,
And overbuilt with most impending brows,
'Twere well, could you permit the World to live
As the World pleases : what's the World to you ?
Much. I was born of woman, and drew milk
As sweet as charity from human breasts.
I think, articulate, I laugh and weep,
And exercise all functions of a man.
How then should I and any man that lives
Be stranger to each other ? Pierce my vein,
Take of the crimson stream meand'ring there,

And catechise it well ; apply thy glass,
Search it, and prove now if it be not blood
Congenial with thine own : and, if it be,
What edge of subtlety canst thou suppose
Keen enough, wise and skilful as thou art,
To cut the link of brotherhood, by which
One common Maker bound me to the kind ?
True ; I am no proficient, I confess,
In arts like yours. I cannot call the swift
And perilous lightnings from the angry clouds,
And bid them hide themselves in earth beneath ;
I cannot analyse the air, nor catch
The parallax of yonder luminous point,
That seems half quench'd in the immense abyss :
Such pow'rs I boast not, neither can I rest
A silent witness of the headlong rage,
Or heedless folly, by which thousands die,
Bone of my bone, and kindred souls to mine.

God never meant, that man should scale the
    Heav'ns
By strides of human wisdom, in his works,
Though wondrous : he commands us in his word
To seek him rather, where his mercy shines.
The mind indeed, enlighten'd from above,
Views him in all ; ascribes to the grand cause
The grand effect ; acknowledges with joy
His manner, and with rapture tastes his style.
But never yet did philosophic tube,
That brings the planets home into the eye
Of Observation, and discovers, else
Not visible, his family of worlds,
Discover him, that rules them ; such a veil
Hangs over mortal eyes, blind from the birth,
And dark in things divine. Full often too
Our wayward intellect, the more we learn
Of nature, overlooks her Author more ;
From instrumental causes proud to draw

Conclusions retrograde, and mad mistake.
But if his word once teach us, shoot a ray
Through all the heart's dark chambers, and reveal
Truths undiscern'd but by that holy light,
Then all is plain. Philosophy, batiz'd
In the pure fountain of eternal love,
Has eyes indeed ; and viewing all she sees
As meant to indicate a God to man,
Gives *him* his praise, and forfeits not her own.
Learning has borne such fruit in other days
On all her branches ; piety has found
Friends in the friends of science, and true pray'r
Has flow'd from lips wet with Castalian dews.
Such was thy wisdom, Newton, childlike sage !
Sagacious reader of the works of God,
And in his word sagacious.

From WILLIAM COWPER, *The Task*, Book III (1785)

STEAM

NYMPHS ! you erewhile on simmering cauldrons play'd,
And call'd delighted Savery to your aid ;
Bade round the youth explosive steam aspire
In gathering clouds, and wing'd the wave with fire ;
Bade with cold streams the quick expansion stop,
And sunk the immense of vapour to a drop. —
Press'd by the ponderous air the piston falls
Resistless, sliding through its iron walls ;
Quick moves the balanced beam, of giant-birth,
Wields his large limbs, and nodding shakes the earth.
  'The giant-power from earth's remotest caves
Lifts with strong arm her dark reluctant waves ;
Each cavern'd rock, and hidden den explores,
Drags her dark coals, and digs her shining ores. —
Next, in close cells of ribbed oak confined,
Gale after gale, he crowds the struggling wind ;

The imprison'd storms through brazen nostrils roar,
Fan the white flame, and fuse the sparkling ore.
Here high in air the rising stream he pours
To clay-built cisterns, or to lead-lined towers ;
Fresh through a thousand pipes the wave distils,
And thirsty cities drink the exuberant rills. —
There the vast mill-stone with inebriate whirl
On trembling floors his forceful fingers twirl.
Whose flinty teeth the golden harvests grind,
Feast without blood ! and nourish human-kind.
  'Now his hard hands on Mona's rifted crest,
Bosom'd in rock, her azure ores arrest ;
With iron lips his rapid rollers seize
The lengthening bars, in thin expansion squeeze ;
Descending screws with ponderous fly-wheels wound
The tawny plates, the new medallions round ;
Hard dyes of steel the cupreous circles cramp,
And with quick fall his massy hammers stamp.
The harp, the lily and the lion join,
And George and Britain guard the sterling coin.
  'Soon shall thy arm, unconquer'd steam ! afar
Drag the slow barge, or drive the rapid car ;
Or on wide-waving wings expanded bear
The flying-chariot through the fields of air.
— Fair crews triumphant, leaning from above,
Shall wave their fluttering kerchiefs as they move ;
Or warrior-bands alarm the gaping crowd,
And armies shrink beneath the shadowy cloud.'

From ERASMUS DARWIN, *The Botanic Garden :* Part 1,
The Economy of Vegetation (1791)

THE LOVES OF THE PLANTS

DESCEND, ye hovering Sylphs ! aerial Quires,
And sweep with little hands your silver lyres ;

With fairy footsteps print your grassy rings,
Ye Gnomes ! accordant to the tinkling strings ;
While in soft notes I tune to oaten reed
Gay hopes, and amorous sorrows of the mead. —
From giant Oaks, that wave their branches dark,
To the dwarf Moss, that clings upon their bark,
What Beaux and Beauties crowd the gaudy groves,
And woo and win their vegetable Loves.
How Snowdrops cold, and blue-eyed Harebels blend
Their tender tears, as o'er the stream they bend ;
The lovesick Violet, and the Primrose pale
Bow their sweet heads, and whisper to the gale ;
With secret sighs the Virgin Lily droops,
And jealous Cowslips hang their tawny cups.
How the young Rose in beauty's damask pride
Drinks the warm blushes of his bashful bride ;
With honey'd lips enamour'd Woodbines meet,
Clasp with fond arms, and mix their kisses sweet. —
　　Stay thy soft-murmuring waters, gentle Rill ;
Hush, whispering Winds, ye rustling Leaves, be still ;
Rest, silver Butterflies, your quivering wings ;
Alight, ye Beetles, from your airy rings ;
Ye painted Moths, your gold-eyed plumage furl,
Bow your wide horns, your spiral trunks uncurl ;
Glitter, ye Glow-worms, on your mossy beds ;
Descend, ye Spiders, on your lengthened threads ;
Slide here, ye horned Snails, with varnish'd shells ;
Ye Bee-nymphs, listen in your waxen cells !
　　Botanic Muse ! who in this latter age
Led by your airy hand the Swedish sage,
Bade his keen eye your secret haunts explore
On dewy dell, high wood, and winding shore ;
Say on each leaf how tiny Graces dwell ;
How laugh the Pleasures in a blossom's bell ;
How insect Loves arise on cobweb wings,
Aim their light shafts, and point their little stings.
　　'First the tall Canna lifts his curled brow
Erect to heaven, and plights his nuptial vow ;

The virtuous pair, in milder regions born,
Dread the rude blast of Autumn's icy morn ;
Round the chill fair he folds his crimson vest,
And clasps the timorous beauty to his breast.

Thy love, Callitriche, *two* Virgins share,
Smit with thy starry eye and radiant hair ; —
On the green margin sits the youth, and loves
His floating train of tresses in the waves ;
Sees his fair features paint the streams that pass,
And bends for ever o'er the watery glass.

Two brother swains, of Collin's gentle name,
The same their features, and their forms the same,
With rival love for fair Collinia sigh,
Knit the dark brow, and roll the unsteady eye.
With sweet concern the pitying beauty mourns,
And soothes with smiles the jealous pair by turns.

Sweet blooms Genista in the myrtle shade,
And *ten* fond brothers woo the haughty maid.
Two Knights before thy fragrant altar bend,
Adored Melissa ! and *two* squires attend.
Meadia's soft chains *five* suppliant beaux confess,
And hand in hand the laughing belle address ;
Alike to all, she bows with wanton air,
Rolls her dark eye, and waves her golden hair.'

From ERASMUS DARWIN, *The Botanic Garden* : Part II,
The Loves of the Plants (1791)

PROFESSIONS — PHYSIC

NEXT, to a graver tribe we turn our view,
And yield the praise to worth and science due ;
But this with serious words and sober style,
For these are friends with whom we seldom smile :
Helpers of men they're call'd, and we confess
Theirs the deep study, theirs the lucky guess.

We own that numbers join with care and skill
A temperate judgement, a devoted will :
Men who suppress their feelings, but who feel
The painful symptoms they delight to heal ;
Patient in all their trials, they sustain
The starts of passion, the reproach of pain ;
With hearts affected, but with looks serene,
Intent they wait through all the solemn scene ;
Glad, if a hope should rise from nature's strife,
To aid their skill and save the lingering life.
But this must virtue's generous effort be,
And spring from nobler motives than a fee :
To the physicians of the soul, and these,
Turn the distress'd for safety, hope, and ease.
    But as physicians of that nobler kind
Have their warm zealots, and their sectaries blind;
So among these for knowledge most renown'd,
Are dreamers strange, and stubborn bigots found.
Some, too, admitted to this honour'd name,
Have, without learning, found a way to fame ;
And some by learning :—young physicians write,
To set their merit in the fairest light ;
With them a treatise is a bait that draws
Approving voices ; 'tis to gain applause,
And to exalt them in the public view,
More than a life of worthy toil could do.
When 'tis proposed to make the man renown'd,
In every age convenient doubts abound ;
Convenient themes in every period start,
Which he may treat with all the pomp of art ;
Curious conjectures he may always make,
And either side of dubious questions take.
He may a system broach, or, if he please,
Start new opinions of an old disease ;
Or may some simple in the woodland trace,
And be its patron, till it runs its race ;
As rustic damsels from their woods are won,
And live in splendour till their race be run ;

It weighs not much on what their powers be shown,
When all his purpose is to make them known.

To show the world what long experience gains,
Requires not courage, though it calls for pains ;
But, at life's outset to inform mankind,
Is a bold effort of a valiant mind.

The great good man, for noblest cause, displays
What many labours taught, and many days ;
These sound instruction from experience give,
The others show us how they mean to live ;
That they have genius, and they hope mankind
Will to its efforts be no longer blind.

There are, beside, whom powerful friends advance,
Whom fashion favours, person, patrons, chance ;
And merit sighs to see a fortune made
By daring rashness or by dull parade.

But these are trifling evils ; there is one
Which walks uncheck'd, and triumphs in the sun :
There was a time, when we beheld the quack,
On public stage, the licensed trade attack ;
He made his labour'd speech with poor parade ;
And then a laughing zany lent him aid.
Smiling we pass'd him, but we felt the while
Pity so much, that soon we ceased to smile ;
Assured that fluent speech and flow'ry vest
Disguised the troubles of a man distress'd.

But now our quacks are gamesters, and they play
With craft and skill to ruin and betray ;
With monstrous promise they delude the mind,
And thrive on all that tortures human-kind.

Void of all honour, avaricious, rash,
The daring tribe compound their boasted trash —
Tincture or syrup, lotion, drop or pill ;
All tempt the sick to trust the lying bill ;
And twenty names of cobblers turn'd to squires,
Aid the bold language of these blushless liars.
There are among them those who cannot read,
And yet they'll buy a patent, and succeed ;

Will dare to promise dying sufferers aid, —
For who, when dead, can threaten or upbraid ?
With cruel avarice still they recommend
More draughts, more syrup, to the journey's end :
'I feel it not ;' — 'Then take it every hour.' —
'It makes me worse ;' — 'Why, then it shows its power.' —
'I fear to die ;' — 'Let not your spirits sink,
'You're always safe, while you believe and drink.'
　How strange to add, in this nefarious trade,
That men of parts are dupes by dunces made :
That creatures nature meant should clean our streets
Have purchased lands and mansions, parks and seats ;
Wretches with conscience so obtuse, they leave
Their untaught sons their parents to deceive ;
And, when they're laid upon their dying-bed,
No thought of murder comes into their head ;
Nor one revengeful ghost to them appears.
To fill the soul with penitential fears.
　Yet not the whole of this imposing train
Their gardens, seats, and carriages obtain ;
Chiefly, indeed, they to the robbers fall,
Who are most fitted to disgrace them all.
But there is hazard — patents must be bought,
Venders and puffers for the poison sought ;
And then in many a paper through the year
Must cures and cases, oaths and proofs appear ;
Men snatch'd from graves, as they were dropping in,
Their lungs cough'd up, their bones pierced through their
　　skin ;
Their liver all one scirrhus, and the frame
Poison'd with evils which they dare not name ;
Men who spent all upon physicians' fees,
Who never slept, nor had a moment's ease,
Are now as roaches sound, and all as brisk as bees.
　If the sick gudgeons to the bait attend,
And come in shoals, the angler gains his end ;
But, should the advertising cash be spent,
Ere yet the town has due attention lent,

Then bursts the bubble, and the hungry cheat
Pines for the bread he ill deserves to eat :
It is a lottery, and he shares perhaps
The rich man's feast, or begs the pauper's scraps.
  From powerful causes spring th' empiric's gains,
Man's love of life, his weakness, and his pains ;
These first induce him the vile trash to try,
Then lend his name, that other men may buy.
This love of life, which in our nature rules,
To vile imposture makes us dupes and tools ;
Then pain compels th' impatient soul to seize
On promised hopes of instantaneous ease ;
And weakness too with every wish complies,
Worn out and won by importunities.

From GEORGE CRABBE, *The Borough* (1810)

MOCK ON, MOCK ON! VOLTAIRE, ROUSSEAU

MOCK on, Mock on, Voltaire, Rousseau ;
Mock on, Mock on ; 'tis all in vain !
You throw the sand against the wind,
And the wind blows it back again.

And every sand becomes a Gem
Reflected in the beams divine ;
Blown back they blind the mocking Eye,
But still in Israel's paths they shine.

The Atoms of Democritus
And Newton's Particles of Light
Are sands upon the Red Sea shore
Where Israel's tents do shine so bright.

WILLIAM BLAKE, written *c.* 1800

William Blake

MEN AND MACHINES

THEN left the sons of Urizen the plow and harrow, the loom,
The hammer and the chisel and the rule and compasses.
They forg'd the sword, the chariot of war, the battle ax,
The trumpet fitted to the battle and the flute of summer,
And all the arts of life they chang'd into the arts of death.
The hour glass contemn'd because its simple workmanship
Was as the workmanship of the plowman, and the water
    wheel
That raises water into Cisterns, broken and burn'd in fire
Because its workmanship was like the workmanship of the
    shepherd,
And in their stead intricate wheels invented, Wheel without
    wheel,
To perplex youth in their outgoings and to bind to labours
Of day and night the myriads of Eternity, that they might file
And polish brass and iron hour after hour, laborious work-
    manship,
Kept ignorant of the use that they might spend the days of
    wisdom
In sorrowful drudgery to obtain a scanty pittance of bread,
In ignorance to view a small portion and think that All,
And call it demonstration, blind to all the simple rules of life.

From WILLIAM BLAKE, *Vala, or the Four Zoas,*
Night the Seventh, written 1795–1804

THE LOVES OF THE TRIANGLES

(*Parody — Erasmus Darwin*)

STAY your rude steps, or e'er your feet invade
The Muses' haunts, ye Sons of War and Trade !
Nor you, ye Legion Fiends of Church and Law,
Pollute these pages with unhallow'd paw !

Debased, corrupted, groveling, and confined,
No DEFINITIONS touch your senseless mind ;
To you no POSTULATES prefer their claim,
No ardent AXIOMS your dull souls inflame ;
For you no TANGENTS touch, no ANGLES meet,
No CIRCLES join in osculation sweet !

For me, ye CISSOIDS, round my temples bend
Your wandering Curves ; ye CONCHOIDS extend ;
Let playful PENDULES quick vibration feel,
While silent CYCLOIS rests upon her wheel ;
Let HYDROSTATICS, simpering as they go,
Lead the light Naiads on fantastic toe ;
Let shrill ACOUSTICS tune the tiny lyre ;
With EUCLID sage fair ALGEBRA conspire ;
The obedient pulley strong MECHANICS ply,
And wanton OPTICS roll the melting eye !

I see the fair fantastic forms appear,
The flaunting drapery and the languid leer ;
Fair Sylphish forms — who, tall, erect, and slim,
Dart the keen glance, and stretch the length of limb ;
To viewless harpings weave the meanless dance,
Wave the gay wreath, and titter as they prance.

Such rich confusion charms the ravish'd sight,
When vernal Sabbaths to the Park invite ;
Mounts the thick dust, the coaches crowd along,
Presses round Grosvenor Gate the impatient throng ;
White-muslin'd misses and mammas are seen,
Link'd with gay Cockneys glittering o'er the green :
The rising breeze unnumber'd charms displays,
And the tight ankle strikes th' astonish'd gaze.

But chief, thou Nurse of the Didactic Muse,
Divine NONSENSIA, all thy sense infuse ;
The charms of Secants and of Tangents tell,
How Loves and Graces in an Angle dwell ;

How slow progressive Points protract the Line,
As pendant spiders spin the filmy twine ;
How lengthened Lines, impetuous sweeping round,
Spread the wide Plane, and mark its circling bound ;
How Planes, their substance with their motion grown,
Form the huge Cube, the Cylinder, the Cone.

.   .   .   .   .

'Twas thine alone, O youth of giant frame,
Isosceles ! that rebel heart to tame !
In vain coy Mathesis thy presence flies,
Still turn her fond hallucinating eyes ;
Thrills with Galvanic fires each tortuous nerve,
Throb her blue veins, and dies her cold reserve ;
— Yet strives the fair, till in the Giant's breast
She sees the mutual passion flame confess'd :
Where'er he moves she sees his tall limbs trace
Internal Angles equal at the Base ;
Again she doubts him : but produced at will,
She sees the external Angles equal still.

Say, blest Isosceles ! what favouring pow'r,
Or love, or chance, at night's auspicious hour,
While to the Asses'-Bridge entranced you stray'd,
Led to the Asses'-Bridge the enamour'd maid ?
— The Asses'-Bridge, for ages doom'd to hear
The deafening surge assault his wooden ear,
With joy repeats sweet sounds of mutual bliss,
The soft susurrant sigh, and gently-murmuring kiss.

JOHN HOOKHAM FRERE and GEORGE CANNING, in the
Anti-Jacobin, or Weekly Examiner (1798)

NEWTON'S STATUE AT TRINITY COLLEGE, CAMBRIDGE

THE Evangelist St. John my patron was :
Three Gothic courts are his, and in the first

Was my abiding-place, a nook obscure;
Right underneath, the College kitchens made
A humming sound, less tuneable than bees,
But hardly less industrious; with shrill notes
Of sharp command and scolding intermixed.
Near me hung Trinity's loquacious clock,
Who never let the quarters, night or day,
Slip by him unproclaimed, and told the hours
Twice over with a male and female voice.
Her pealing organ was my neighbour too;
And from my pillow, looking forth by light
Of moon or favouring stars, I could behold
The antechapel where the statue stood
Of Newton with his prism and silent face,
The marble index of a mind for ever
Voyaging through strange seas of Thought, alone.

From WILLIAM WORDSWORTH, *The Prelude*,
Book III (1850), written 1799–1805

GEOMETRY

YET may we not entirely overlook
The pleasure gathered from the rudiments
Of geometric science. Though advanced
In these enquiries, with regret I speak,
No farther than the threshold, there I found
Both elevation and composed delight:
With Indian awe and wonder, ignorance pleased
With its own struggles, did I meditate
On the relation those abstractions bear
To Nature's laws, and by what process led,
Those immaterial agents bowed their heads
Duly to serve the mind of earth-born man;
From star to star, from kindred sphere to sphere,
From system on to system without end.

More frequently from the same source I drew
A pleasure quiet and profound, a sense
Of permanent and universal sway,
And paramount belief ; there, recognised
A type, for finite natures, of the one
Supreme Existence, the surpassing life
Which — to the boundaries of space and time,
Of melancholy space and doleful time,
Superior and incapable of change,
Nor touched by welterings of passion — is,
And hath the name of, God.   Transcendent peace
And silence did await upon these thoughts
That were a frequent comfort to my youth.

'Tis told by one whom stormy waters threw,
With fellow-sufferers by the shipwreck spared,
Upon a desert coast, that having brought
To land a single volume, saved by chance,
A treatise of Geometry, he wont,
Although of food and clothing destitute,
And beyond common wretchedness depressed,
To part from company and take this book
(Then first a self-taught pupil in its truths)
To spots remote, and draw his diagrams
With a long staff upon the sand, and thus
Did oft beguile his sorrow, and almost
Forget his feeling : so (if like effect
From the same cause produced, 'mid outward things
So different, may rightly be compared),
So was it then with me, and so will be
With Poets ever.   Mighty is the charm
Of those abstractions to a mind beset
With images and haunted by herself,
And specially delightful unto me
Was that clear synthesis built up aloft
So gracefully ; even then when it appeared
Not more than a mere plaything, or a toy
To sense embodied : not the thing it is

In verity, an independent world,
Created out of pure intelligence.

From WILLIAM WORDSWORTH, *The Prelude*,
Book VI (1850), written 1799–1805

THE INDUSTRIAL REVOLUTION

'HAPPY,' rejoined the Wanderer, 'they who gain
A panegyric from your generous tongue !
But, if to these Wayfarers once pertained
Aught of romantic interest, it is gone.
Their purer service, in this realm at least,
Is past for ever. — An inventive Age
Has wrought, if not with speed of magic, yet
To most strange issues. I have lived to mark
A new and unforeseen creation rise
From out the labours of a peaceful Land
Wielding her potent enginery to frame
And to produce, with appetite as keen
As that of war, which rests not night or day,
Industrious to destroy ! With fruitless pains
Might one like me *now* visit many a tract
Which, in his youth, he trod, and trod again,
A lone pedestrian with a scanty freight,
Wished-for, or welcome, wheresoe'er he came —
Among the tenantry of thorpe and vill ;
Or straggling burgh, of ancient charter proud,
And dignified by battlements and towers
Of some stern castle, mouldering on the brow
Of a green hill or bank of rugged stream.
The foot-path faintly marked, the horse-track wild,
And formidable length of plashy lane,
(Prized avenues ere others had been shaped
Or easier links connecting place with place)

Have vanished — swallowed up by stately roads
Easy and bold, that penetrate the gloom
Of Britain's farthest glens.   The Earth has lent
Her waters, Air her breezes ; and the sail
Of traffic glides with ceaseless intercourse,
Glistening along the low and woody dale ;
Or, in its progress, on the lofty side,
Of some bare hill, with wonder kenned from far.

'Meanwhile, at social Industry's command,
How quick, how vast an increase !   From the germ
Of some poor hamlet, rapidly produced
Here a huge town, continuous and compact,
Hiding the face of earth for leagues — and there,
Where not a habitation stood before,
Abodes of men irregularly massed
Like trees in forests, — spread through spacious tracts,
O'er which the smoke of unremitting fires
Hangs permanent, and plentiful as wreaths
Of vapour glittering in the morning sun.
And, wheresoe'er the traveller turns his steps,
He sees the barren wilderness erased,
Or disappearing ; triumph that proclaims
How much the mild Directress of the plough
Owes to alliance with these new-born arts !
— Hence is the wide sea peopled, — hence the shores
Of Britain are resorted to by ships
Freighted from every climate of the world
With the world's choicest produce.   Hence that sum
Of keels that rest within her crowded ports,
Or ride at anchor in her sounds and bays ;
That animating spectacle of sails
That, through her inland regions, to and fro
Pass with the respirations of the tide,
Perpetual, multitudinous !   Finally,
Hence a dread arm of floating power, a voice
Of thunder daunting those who would approach
With hostile purposes the blessèd Isle,

Truth's consecrated residence, the seat
Impregnable of Liberty and Peace.

'And yet, O happy Pastor of a flock
Faithfully watched, and, by that loving care
And Heaven's good providence, preserved from taint !
With you I grieve, when on the darker side
Of this great change I look ; and there behold
Such outrage done to nature as compels
The indignant power to justify herself ;
Yea, to avenge her violated rights,
For England's bane. — When soothing darkness spreads
O'er hill and vale,' the Wanderer thus expressed
His recollections, 'and the punctual stars,
While all things else are gathering to their homes,
Advance, and in the firmament of heaven
Glitter — but undisturbing, undisturbed ;
As if their silent company were charged
With peaceful admonitions for the heart
Of all-beholding Man, earth's thoughtful lord ;
Then, in full many a region, once like this
The assured domain of calm simplicity
And pensive quiet, an unnatural light
Prepared for never-resting Labour's eyes
Breaks from a many-windowed fabric huge ;
And at the appointed hour a bell is heard —
Of harsher import than the curfew-knoll
That spake the Norman Conqueror's stern behest —
A local summons to unceasing toil !
Disgorged are now the ministers of day ;
And, as they issue from the illumined pile,
A fresh band meets them, at the crowded door —
And in the courts — and where the rumbling stream,
That turns the multitude of dizzy wheels,
Glares, like a troubled spirit, in its bed
Among the rocks below.   Men, maidens, youths,
Mother and little children, boys and girls,
Enter, and each the wonted task resumes

Within this temple, where is offered up
To Gain, the master idol of the realm,
Perpetual sacrifice. Even thus of old
Our ancestors, within the still domain
Of vast cathedral or conventual church,
Their vigils kept ; where tapers day and night
On the dim altar burned continually,
In token that the House was evermore
Watching to God. Religious men were they ;
Nor would their reason, tutored to aspire
Above this transitory world, allow
That there should pass a moment of the year,
When in their land the Almighty's service ceased.

   'Triumph who will in these profaner rites
Which we, a generation self-extolled,
As zealously perform ! I cannot share
His proud complacency : — yet do I exult,
Casting reserve away, exult to see
An intellectual mastery exercised
O'er the blind elements ; a purpose given,
A perseverance fed ; almost a soul
Imparted — to brute matter. I rejoice,
Measuring the force of those gigantic powers
That, by the thinking mind, have been compelled
To serve the will of feeble-bodied Man.
For with the sense of admiration blends
The animating hope that time may come
When, strengthened, yet not dazzled, by the might
Of this dominion over nature gained,
Men of all lands shall exercise the same
In due proportion to their country's need,
Learning, though late, that all true glory rests,
All praise, all safety, and all happiness,
Upon the moral law. Egyptian Thebes,
Tyre, by the margin of the sounding waves,
Palmyra, central in the desert, fell ;
And the Arts died by which they had been raised.

— Call Archimedes from his buried tomb
Upon the grave of vanished Syracuse,
And feelingly the Sage shall make report
How insecure, how baseless in itself,
Is the Philosophy whose sway depends
On mere material instruments ; — how weak
Those arts, and high inventions, if unpropped
By virtue. — He, sighing with pensive grief,
Amid his calm abstractions, would admit
That not the slender privilege is theirs
To save themselves from blank forgetfulness !'

From WILLIAM WORDSWORTH, *The Excursion*,
Book VIII (1814)

INSIDE OF KING'S COLLEGE CHAPEL, CAMBRIDGE

TAX not the royal Saint with vain expense,
With ill-matched aims the Architect who planned —
Albeit labouring for a scanty band
Of white-robed Scholars only — this immense
And glorious Work of fine intelligence !
Give all thou canst ; high Heaven rejects the lore
Of nicely-calculated less or more ;
So deemed the man who fashioned for the sense
These lofty pillars, spread that branching roof
Self-poised, and scooped into ten thousand cells,
Where light and shade repose, where music dwells
Lingering — and wandering on as loth to die ;
Like thoughts whose very sweetness yieldeth proof
That they were born for immortality.

WILLIAM WORDSWORTH, written 1821

STEAMBOATS, VIADUCTS, AND RAILWAYS

MOTIONS and Means, on land and sea at war
With old poetic feeling, not for this,
Shall ye, by Poets even, be judged amiss !
Nor shall your presence, howsoe'er it mar
The loveliness of Nature, prove a bar
To the Mind's gaining that prophetic sense
Of future change, that point of vision, whence
May be discovered what in soul ye are.
In spite of all that beauty may disown
In your harsh features, Nature doth embrace
Her lawful offspring in Man's art ; and Time,
Pleased with your triumphs o'er his brother Space,
Accepts from your bold hands the proffered crown
Of hope, and smiles on you with cheer sublime.

WILLIAM WORDSWORTH, written 1833

ON THE PROJECTED KENDAL AND WINDERMERE RAILWAY

Is then no nook of English ground secure
From rash assault ?   Schemes of retirement sown
In youth, and 'mid the busy world kept pure
As when their earliest flowers of hope were blown,
Must perish ; — how can they this blight endure ?
And must he too the ruthless change bemoan
Who scorns a false utilitarian lure
'Mid his paternal fields at random thrown ?
Baffle the threat, bright Scene, from Orrest-head
Given to the pausing traveller's rapturous glance :
Plead for thy peace, thou beautiful romance
Of nature ; and, if human hearts be dead,

Speak, passing winds ; ye torrents, with your strong
And constant voice, protest against the wrong.

WILLIAM WORDSWORTH, written 1844

THE NATURE OF MATTER AND ENERGY

A SPHERE, which is as many thousand spheres,
Solid as crystal, yet through all its mass
Flow, as through empty space, music and light :
Ten thousand orbs involving and involved,
Purple and azure, white, and green, and golden,
Sphere within sphere ; and every space between
Peopled with unimaginable shapes,
Such as ghosts dream dwell in the lampless deep,
Yet each inter-transpicuous, and they whirl
Over each other with a thousand motions,
Upon a thousand sightless axles spinning,
And with the force of self-destroying swiftness,
Intensely, slowly, solemnly roll on.

From PERCY BYSSHE SHELLEY, *Prometheus Unbound*,
Act IV (1820)

THE CLOUD

I BRING fresh showers for the thirsting flowers,
From the seas and the streams ;
I bear light shade for the leaves when laid
In their noonday dreams.
From my wings are shaken the dews that waken
The sweet buds every one,
When rocked to rest on their mother's breast,
As she dances about the sun.

I wield the flail of the lashing hail,
    And whiten the green plains under,
And then again I dissolve it in rain,
    And laugh as I pass in thunder.

I sift the snow on the mountains below,
    And their great pines groan aghast ;
And all the night 'tis my pillow white,
    While I sleep in the arms of the blast.
Sublime on the towers of my skiey bowers,
    Lightning my pilot sits ;
In a cavern under is fettered the thunder,
    It struggles and howls at fits ;
Over earth and ocean, with gentle motion,
    This pilot is guiding me,
Lured by the love of the genii that move
    In the depths of the purple sea ;
Over the rills, and the crags, and the hills,
    Over the lakes and the plains,
Wherever he dream, under mountain or stream,
    The Spirit he loves remains ;
And I all the while bask in Heaven's blue smile,
    Whilst he is dissolving in rains.

The sanguine Sunrise, with his meteor eyes,
    And his burning plumes outspread,
Leaps on the back of my sailing rack,
    When the morning star shines dead ;
As on the jag of a mountain crag,
    Which an earthquake rocks and swings,
An eagle alit one moment may sit
    In the light of its golden wings.
And when Sunset may breathe, from the lit sea
        beneath,
    Its ardours of rest and of love,
And the crimson pall of eve may fall
    From the depth of Heaven above,

With wings folded I rest, on mine aëry nest,
    As still as a brooding dove.

That orbèd maiden with white fire laden,
    Whom mortals call the Moon,
Glides glimmering o'er my fleece-like floor,
    By the midnight breezes strewn ;
And wherever the beat of her unseen feet,
    Which only the angels hear,
May have broken the woof of my tent's thin roof
    The stars peep behind her and peer ;
And I laugh to see them whirl and flee,
    Like a swarm of golden bees,
When I widen the rent in my wind-built tent,
    Till the calm rivers, lakes, and seas,
Like strips of the sky fallen through me on high,
    Are each paved with the moon and these.

I bind the Sun's throne with a burning zone,
    And the Moon's with a girdle of pearl ;
The volcanoes are dim, and the stars reel and swim,
    When the whirlwinds my banner unfurl.
From cape to cape, with a bridge-like shape,
    Over a torrent sea,
Sunbeam-proof, I hang like a roof, —
    The mountains its columns be,
The triumphal arch through which I march
    With hurricane, fire, and snow,
When the Powers of the air are chained to my chair,
    Is the million-coloured bow ;
The sphere-fire above its soft colours wove,
    While the moist Earth was laughing below.

I am the daughter of Earth and Water,
    And the nursling of the Sky ;
I pass through the pores of the ocean and shores ;
    I change, but I cannot die.

For after the rain when with never a stain
    The pavilion of Heaven is bare,
And the winds and sunbeams with their convex gleams
    Build up the blue dome of air,
I silently laugh at my own cenotaph,
    And out of the caverns of rain,
Like a child from the womb, like a ghost from the
       tomb,
    I arise and unbuild it again.

               PERCY BYSSHE SHELLEY, written 1820

COLD PHILOSOPHY

  WHAT wreath for Lamia ?   What for Lycius ?
What for the sage, old Apollonius ?
Upon her aching forehead be there hung
The leaves of willow and of adder's tongue ;
And for the youth, quick, let us strip for him
The thyrsus, that his watching eyes may swim
Into forgetfulness ; and, for the sage,
Let spear-grass and the spiteful thistle wage
War on his temples.   Do not all charms fly
At the mere touch of cold philosophy ?
There was an awful rainbow once in heaven :
We know her woof, her texture ; she is given
In the dull catalogue of common things.
Philosophy will clip an Angel's wings,
Conquer all mysteries by rule and line,
Empty the haunted air, and gnomed mine —
Unweave a rainbow, as it erewhile made
The tender-person'd Lamia melt into a shade.

            From JOHN KEATS, *Lamia* (1820)

ODE TO MR. M‘ADAM

1

M‘ADAM, hail !
Hail, Roadian ! hail, Colossus ! who dost stand
Striding ten thousand turnpikes on the land !
  Oh universal Leveller ! all hail !
To thee, a good, yet stony-hearted man,
  The kindest one, and yet the flintiest going, —
To thee, — how much for thy commodious plan,
  Lanark Reformer of the Ruts, is Owing !
    The Bristol mail,
Gliding o'er ways hitherto deem'd invincible,
  When carrying Patriots now shall never fail
Those of the most '*unshaken* public principle.'
    Hail to thee, Scot of Scots !
  Thou northern light, amid those heavy men !
Foe to Stonehenge, yet friend to all beside,
Thou scatter'st flints and favours far and wide,
    From palaces to cots ; —
    Dispenser of coagulated good !
    Distributor of granite and of food !
Long may thy fame its even path march on,
  E'en when thy sons are dead !
Best benefactor ! though thou giv'st a stone
  To those who ask for bread !

2

Thy first great trial in this mighty town
Was, if I rightly recollect, upon
    That gentle hill which goeth
Down from 'the County' to the Palace gate,
  And, like a river, thanks to thee, now floweth
Past the Old Horticultural Society, —
The chemist Cobb's, the house of Howell and James,
Where ladies play high shawl and satin games —
    A little *Hell* of lace !

And past the Athenæum, made of late,
    Severs a sweet variety
Of milliners and booksellers who grace
    Waterloo Place,
Making division, the Muse fears and guesses,
'Twixt Mr. Rivington's and Mr. Hessey's,
Thou stood'st thy trial, Mac ! and shav'd the road
From Barber Beaumont's to the King's abode
So well, that paviours threw their rammers by,
Let down their tuck'd shirt-sleeves, and with a sigh
Prepar'd themselves, poor souls, to chip or die !

3

Next, from the palace to the prison, thou
    Didst go, the highway's watchman, to thy beat, —
    Preventing though the *rattling* in the street,
        Yet kicking up a row
Upon the stones — ah ! truly watchman-like,
Encouraging thy victims all to strike,
    To further thy own purpose, Adam, daily ; —
Thou hast smooth'd, alas, the path to the Old Bailey !
        And to the stony bowers
    Of Newgate, to encourage the approach,
        By caravan or coach, —
Hast strew'd the way with flints as soft as flowers.

4

    Who shall dispute thy name !
    Insculpt in stone in every street,
        We soon shall greet
    Thy trodden down, yet all unconquer'd fame !
Where'er we take, even at this time, our way,
Nought see we, but mankind in open air,
Hammering thy fame, as Chantrey would not dare ; —
        And with a patient care,
Chipping thy immortality all day !
Demosthenes, of old — that rare old man —
Prophetically, *follow'd*, Mac ! thy plan :—

For he, we know,
(History says so,)
Put *pebbles* in his mouth when he would speak
The *smoothest* Greek !

5

It is 'impossible, and cannot be,'
But that thy genius hath,
Besides the turnpike, many another path
Trod, to arrive at popularity.
O'er Pegasus, perchance, thou hast thrown a thigh,
Nor ridden a roadster only ; mighty Mac !
And 'faith I'd swear, when on that winged hack,
Thou hast observ'd the highways in the sky !
Is the path up Parnassus rough and steep,
And 'hard to climb,' as Dr. B. would say ?
Dost think it best for Sons of Song to keep
The noiseless *tenor* of their way ? (see Gray.)
What line of road *should* poets take to bring
Themselves unto those waters, lov'd the first !
Those waters which can wet a man to sing !
Which, like thy fame, 'from *granite* basins burst,
Leap into life, and, sparkling, woo the thirst ?'

6

— That thou'rt a proser, even thy birth-place might
Vouchsafe ; — and Mr. Cadell *may*, God wot,
Have paid thee many a pound for many a blot, —
Cadell's a wayward wight !
Although no Walter, still thou art a Scot,
And I can throw, I think, a little light
Upon some works thou hast written for the town, —
And publish'd, like a Lilliput Unknown !
'Highways and Byeways,' is thy book, no doubt,
(One whole edition's out,)
And next, for it is fair
That Fame,
Seeing her children, should confess she had 'em ; —

'Some *Passages* from the life of Adam Blair,' —
        (Blair is a Scottish name,)
What are they, but thy own good roads, M'Adam?

7

        O ! indefatigable labourer
In the paths of men ! when thou shalt die, 'twill be
A mark of thy surpassing industry,
    That of the monument, which men shall rear
Over thy most inestimable bone,
Thou didst thy very self lay the first stone ! —
Of a right ancient line thou comest, — through
Each crook and turn we trace the unbroken clue,
Until we see thy sire before our eyes, —
Rolling his gravel walks in Paradise !
But he, our great Mac Parent, err'd, and ne'er
        Have our walks since been fair !
Yet Time, who, like the merchant, lives on 'Change,
For ever varying, through his varying range,
        Time maketh all things even !
In this strange world, turning beneath high heaven !
    He hath redeem'd the Adams, and contrived, —
        (How are Time's wonders hiv'd !)
    In pity to mankind and to befriend 'em —
        (Time is above all praise,)
That he, who first did make our evil ways,
Reborn in Scotland, should be first to mend 'em !

        JOHN HAMILTON REYNOLDS, *Odes and Addresses*
                    to Great People (1825)

CRANIOLOGY

    'TIS strange how like a very dunce,
    Man — with his bumps upon his sconce,
    Has lived so long, and yet no knowledge he
    Has had, till lately, of Phrenology —
    A science that by simple dint of

Head-combing he should find a hint of,
When scratching o'er those little pole-hills,
The faculties throw up like mole-hills ; —
A science that, in very spite
Of all his teeth, ne'er came to light,
For though he knew his skull had *grinders*,
Still there turn'd up no *organ* finders,
Still sages wrote, and ages fled,
And no man's head came in his head —
Not even the pate of Erra Pater,
Knew aught about its pia mater.
At last great Dr. Gall bestirs him —
I don't know but it might be Spurzheim —
Tho' native of a dull and slow land,
And makes partition of our Poll-land,
At our Acquisitiveness guesses,
And all those necessary *nesses*
Indicative of human habits,
All burrowing in the head like rabbits.
Thus Veneration, he made known,
Had got a lodging at the Crown :
And Music (see Deville's example)
A set of chambers in the Temple :
That Language taught the tongues close by,
And took in pupils thro' the eye,
Close by his neighbour Computation,
Who taught the eyebrows numeration.

The science thus — to speak in fit
Terms — having struggled from its nit,
Was seiz'd on by a swarm of Scotchmen
Those scientifical hotch-potch men,
Who have at least a penny dip
And wallop in all doctorship,
Just as in making broth they smatter
By bobbing twenty things in water :
These men, I say, make quick appliance
And close, to phrenologic science ;

For of all learned themes whatever,
That schools and colleges deliver,
There's none they love so near the bodles,
As analyzing their own noddles ;
Thus in a trice each northern blockhead
Had got his fingers in his shock head,
And of his bumps was babbling yet worse
Than poor Miss Capulet's dry wet-nurse ;
Till having been sufficient rangers
Of their own heads, they took to strangers',
And found in Presbyterians' polls
The things they hated in their souls ;
For Presbyterians hear with passion
Of organs join'd with veneration.
No kind there was of human pumpkin,
But at its bumps it had a bumpkin ;
Down to the very lowest gullion,
And oiliest scull of oily scullion.
No great man died but this they *did* do,
They begg'd his cranium of his widow :
No murderer died by law disaster,
But they took off his sconce in plaster ;
For thereon they could show depending,
'The head and front of his offending,'
How that his philanthropic bump
Was master'd by a baser lump ;
For every bump (these wags insist)
Has its direct antagonist,
Each striving stoutly to prevail,
Like horses knotted tail to tail ;
And many a stiff and sturdy battle
Occurs between these adverse cattle,
The secret cause, beyond all question,
Of aches ascribed to indigestion, —
Whereas 'tis but two knobby rivals
Tugging together like sheer devils,
Till one gets mastery good or sinister,
And comes in like a new prime-minister.

Each bias in some master node is :—
What takes M'Adam where a road is,
To hammer little pebbles less ?
His organ of destructiveness.
What makes great Joseph so encumber
Debate ?   a lumping lump of Number :
Or Malthus rail at babies so ?
The smallness of his Philopro —
What severs man and wife ?   a simple
Defect of the Adhesive pimple :
Or makes weak women go astray ?
Their bumps are more in fault than they.

These facts being found and set in order
By grave M.D.'s beyond the Border,
To make them for some months eternal,
Were enter'd monthly in a journal,
That many a northern sage still writes in,
And throws his little Northern Lights in,
And proves and proves about the phrenos,
A great deal more than I or he knows.
How Music suffers, *par exemple*,
By wearing tight hats round the temple ;
What ills great boxers have to fear
From blisters put behind the ear :
And how a porter's Veneration
Is hurt by porter's occupation :
Whether shillelaghs in reality
May deaden Individuality :
Or tongs and poker be creative
Of alterations in th' Amative :
If falls from scaffolds make us less
Inclin'd to all Constructiveness :
With more such matters, all applying
To heads — and therefore *head*ifying.

THOMAS HOOD, *Whims and Oddities,*
second series (1827)

124

THE CRY OF THE CHILDREN

I

Do ye hear the children weeping, O my brothers,
  Ere the sorrow comes with years ?
They are leaning their young heads against their mothers,
  And *that* cannot stop their tears.
The young lambs are bleating in the meadows,
  The young birds are chirping in the nest,
The young fawns are playing with the shadows,
  The young flowers are blowing toward the west —
But the young, young children, O my brothers,
  They are weeping bitterly !
They are weeping in the playtime of the others,
  In the country of the free.

2

Do you question the young children in the sorrow
  Why their tears are falling so ?
The old man may weep for his to-morrow
  Which is lost in Long Ago ;
The old tree is leafless in the forest,
  The old year is ending in the frost,
The old wound, if stricken, is the sorest,
  The old hope is hardest to be lost :
But the young, young children, O my brothers,
  Do you ask them why they stand
Weeping sore before the bosoms of their mothers,
  In our happy Fatherland ?

3

They look up with their pale and sunken faces,
  And their looks are sad to see,
For the man's hoary anguish draws and presses
  Down the cheeks of infancy ;
'Your old earth,' they say, 'is very dreary,
  Our young feet,' they say, 'are very weak ;

Few paces have we taken, yet are weary —
    Our grave-rest is very far to seek :
Ask the aged why they weep, and not the children,
    For the outside earth is cold,
And we young ones stand without, in our bewildering,
    And the graves are for the old.

4

'True,' say the children, 'it may happen
    That we die before our time :
Little Alice died last year, her grave is shapen
    Like a snowball, in the rime.
We looked into the pit prepared to take her :
    Was no room for any work in the close clay !
From the sleep wherein she lieth none will wake her,
    Crying, "Get up, little Alice ! it is day."
If you listen by that grave, in sun and shower,
    With your ear down, little Alice never cries ;
Could we see her face, be sure we should not know her,
    For the smile has time for growing in her eyes :
And merry go her moments, lulled and stilled in
    The shroud by the kirk-chime.
It is good when it happens,' say the children,
    'That we die before our time.'

5

Alas, alas, the children ! they are seeking
    Death in life, as best to have :
They are binding up their hearts away from breaking,
    With a cerement from the grave.
Go out, children, from the mine and from the city,
    Sing out, children, as the little thrushes do ;
Pluck your handfuls of the meadow-cowslips pretty,
    Laugh aloud, to feel your fingers let them through !
But they answer, 'Are your cowslips of the meadows
    Like our weeds anear the mine ?
Leave us quiet in the dark of the coal-shadows,
    From your pleasures fair and fine !

6

'For oh,' say the children, 'we are weary,
　　And we cannot run or leap ;
If we cared for any meadows, it were merely
　　To drop down in them and sleep.
Our knees tremble sorely in the stooping,
　　We fall upon our faces, trying to go ;
And, underneath our heavy eyelids drooping
　　The reddest flower would look as pale as snow.
For, all day, we drag our burden tiring
　　Through the coal-dark, underground ;
Or, all day, we drive the wheels of iron
　　In the factories, round and round.

7

'For all day the wheels are droning, turning ;
　　Their wind comes in our faces,
Till our hearts turn, our heads with pulses burning,
　　And the walls turn in their places :
Turns the sky in the high window, blank and reeling,
　　Turns the long light that drops adown the wall,
Turn the black flies that crawl along the ceiling :
　　All are turning, all the day, and we with all.
And all day the iron wheels are droning,
　　And sometimes we could pray,
"O ye wheels" (breaking out in a mad moaning),
　　"Stop ! be silent for to-day !"'

8

Ay, be silent ! Let them hear each other breathing
　　For a moment, mouth to mouth !
Let them touch each other's hands, in a fresh wreathing
　　Of their tender human youth !
Let them feel that this cold metallic motion
　　Is not all the life God fashions or reveals :
Let them prove their living souls against the notion
　　That they live in you, or under you, O wheels !

Still, all day, the iron wheels go onward,
    Grinding life down from its mark ;
And the children's souls, which God is calling sunward,
    Spin on blindly in the dark.

9

Now tell the poor young children, O my brothers,
    To look up to Him and pray ;
So the blessed One who blesseth all the others,
    Will bless them another day.
They answer, 'Who is God that He should hear us,
    While the rushing of the iron wheels is stirred ?
When we sob aloud, the human creatures near us
    Pass by, hearing not, or answer not a word.
And *we* hear not (for the wheels in their resounding)
    Strangers speaking at the door :
Is it likely God, with angels singing round Him,
    Hears our weeping any more ?

10

'Two words, indeed, of praying we remember,
    And at midnight's hour of harm,
"Our Father," looking upward in the chamber,
    We say softly for a charm.
We know no other words except "Our Father,"
    And we think that, in some pause of angels' song,
God may pluck them with the silence sweet to gather,
    And hold both within His right hand which is strong.
"Our Father !" If He heard us, He would surely
    (For they call Him good and mild)
Answer, smiling down the steep world very purely,
    "Come and rest with me, my child."

11

'But, no !' say the children, weeping faster,
    'He is speechless as a stone :
And they tell us, of His image is the master
    Who commands us to work on.

Go to !' say the children, — 'up in Heaven,
  Dark, wheel-like, turning clouds are all we find.
Do not mock us ; grief has made us unbelieving :
  We look up for God, but tears have made us blind.'
Do you hear the children weeping and disproving,
    O my brothers, what ye preach ?
For God's possible is taught by His world's loving,
  And the children doubt of each.

12

And well may the children weep before you !
  They are weary ere they run ;
They have never seen the sunshine, nor the glory
  Which is brighter than the sun.
They know the grief of man, without its wisdom ;
  They sink in man's despair, without its calm ;
Are slaves, without the liberty in Christdom,
  Are martyrs, by the pang without the palm :
Are worn as if with age, yet unretrievingly
  The harvest of its memories cannot reap, —
Are orphans of the earthly love and heavenly.
  Let them weep ! let them weep !

13

They look up with their pale and sunken faces,
  And their look is dread to see,
For they mind you of their angels in high places,
  With eyes turned on Deity.
'How long,' they say, 'how long, O cruel nation,
  Will you stand, to move the world, on a child's heart, —
Stifle down with a mailed heel its palpitation,
  And tread onward to your throne amid the mart ?
Our blood splashes upward, O gold-heaper,
  And your purple shows your path !
But the child's sob in the silence curses deeper
  Than the strong man in his wrath.'

ELIZABETH BARRETT BROWNING, Poems (1844)

SONNET — TO SCIENCE

SCIENCE! true daughter of Old Time thou art!
  Who alterest all things with thy peering eyes.
Why preyest thou thus upon the poet's heart,
  Vulture, whose wings are dull realities?
How should he love thee? or how deem thee wise,
  Who wouldst not leave him in his wandering
To seek for treasure in the jewelled skies,
  Albeit he soared with an undaunted wing?
Hast thou not dragged Diana from her car?
  And driven the Hamadryad from the wood
To seek a shelter in some happier star?
  Hast thou not torn the Naïad from her flood,
The Elfin from the green grass, and from me
The summer dream beneath the tamarind tree?

EDGAR ALLAN POE, written c. 1827

SCIENCE AND PROGRESS

COMRADES, leave me here a little, while as yet 'tis early morn:
Leave me here, and when you want me, sound upon the bugle-
  horn.

'Tis the place, and all around it, as of old, the curlews call,
Dreary gleams about the moorland flying over Locksley
  Hall;

Locksley Hall, that in the distance overlooks the sandy tracts,
And the hollow ocean-ridges roaring into cataracts.

Many a night from yonder ivied casement, ere I went to rest,
Did I look on great Orion sloping slowly to the West.

Many a night I saw the Pleiads, rising thro' the mellow shade,
Glitter like a swarm of fire-flies tangled in a silver braid.

Here about the beach I wander'd, nourishing a youth sublime
With the fairy tales of science, and the long result of Time ;

When the centuries behind me like a fruitful land reposed ;
When I clung to all the present for the promise that it closed :

When I dipt into the future far as human eye could see ;
Saw the Vision of the world, and all the wonder that would be.

. . . . . .

Saw the heavens fill with commerce, argosies of magic sails,
Pilots of the purple twilight, dropping down with costly
    bales ;

Heard the heavens fill with shouting, and there rain'd a
    ghastly dew
From the nations' airy navies grappling in the central blue ;

Far along the world-wide whisper of the south-wind rushing
    warm,
With the standards of the peoples plunging thro' the
    thunder-storm ;

Till the war-drum throbb'd no longer, and the battle-flags
    were furl'd
In the Parliament of man, the Federation of the world.

There the common sense of most shall hold a fretful realm in
    awe,
And the kindly earth shall slumber, lapt in universal law.

So I triumph'd ere my passion sweeping thro' me left me dry,
Left me with the palsied heart, and left me with the
    jaundiced eye ;

Eye, to which all order festers, all things here are out of joint :
Science moves, but slowly slowly, creeping on from point to
    point :

Slowly comes a hungry people, as a lion creeping nigher,
Glares at one that nods and winks behind a slowly-dying fire.

Yet I doubt not thro' the ages one increasing purpose runs,
And the thoughts of men are widen'd with the process of the
    suns.

    .   .   .   .   .

Not in vain the distance beacons.   Forward, forward let us
    range,
Let the great world spin for ever down the ringing grooves
    of change.

Thro' the shadow of the globe we sweep into the younger
    day :
Better fifty years of Europe than a cycle of Cathay.

From ALFRED, LORD TENNYSON, Locksley Hall (1832)

RELIGION AND SCIENCE

[LIV]

OH yet we trust that somehow good
Will be the final goal of ill,
To pangs of nature, sins of will,
Defects of doubt, and taints of blood ;

That nothing walks with aimless feet ;
That not one life shall be destroy'd,
Or cast as rubbish to the void,
When God hath made the pile complete ;

That not a worm is cloven in vain ;
    That not a moth with vain desire
    Is shrivell'd in a fruitless fire,
Or but subserves another's gain.

Behold, we know not anything ;
    I can but trust that good shall fall
    At last — far off — at last, to all,
And every winter change to spring.

So runs my dream : but what am I ?
    An infant crying in the night :
    And infant crying for the light :
And with no language but a cry.

[LV]

The wish, that of the living whole
    No life may fail beyond the grave,
    Derives it not from what we have
The likest God within the soul ?

Are God and Nature then at strife,
    That Nature lends such evil dreams ?
    So careful of the type she seems,
So careless of the single life ;

That I, considering everywhere
    Her secret meaning in her deeds,
    And finding that of fifty seeds
She often brings but one to bear,

I falter where I firmly trod,
    And falling with my weight of cares
    Upon the great world's altar-stairs
That slope thro' darkness up to God,

I stretch lame hands of faith, and grope,
    And gather dust and chaff, and call

To what I feel is Lord of all,
And faintly trust the larger hope.

[LVI]

'So careful of the type?' but no.
From scarped cliff and quarried stone
She cries, 'A thousand types are gone :
I care for nothing, all shall go.

'Thou makest thine appeal to me :
I bring to life, I bring to death :
The spirit does but mean the breath :
I know no more.' And he, shall he,

Man, her last work, who seem'd so fair,
Such splendid purpose in his eyes,
Who roll'd the psalm to wintry skies,
Who built him fanes of fruitless prayer,

Who trusted God was love indeed
And love Creation's final law —
Tho' Nature, red in tooth and claw
With ravine, shriek'd against his creed —

Who loved, who suffer'd countless ills,
Who battled for the True, the Just,
Be blown about the desert dust,
Or seal'd within the iron hills ?

No more ? A monster then, a dream,
A discord. Dragons of the prime,
That tare each other in their slime,
Were mellow music match'd with him.

O life as futile, then, as frail !
O for thy voice to soothe and bless !
What hope of answer, or redress ?
Behind the veil, behind the veil.

[LVII]

Peace ; come away : the song of woe
    Is after all an earthly song :
    Peace ; come away : we do him wrong
To sing so wildly : let us go.

        From ALFRED, LORD TENNYSON, *In Memoriam*
                        A. H. H. (1850)

EVOLUTION

[CXVIII]

CONTEMPLATE all this work of Time,
    The giant labouring in his youth ;
    Nor dream of human love and truth,
As dying Nature's earth and lime ;

But trust that those we call the dead
    Are breathers of an ampler day
    For ever nobler ends.   They say,
The solid earth whereon we tread

In tracts of fluent heat began,
    And grew to seeming-random forms,
    The seeming prey of cyclic storms,
Till at the last arose the man ;

Who throve and branch'd from clime to clime,
    The herald of a higher race,
    And of himself in higher place,
If so he type this work of time

Within himself, from more to more ;
    Or, crown'd with attributes of woe
    Like glories, move his course, and show
That life is not as idle ore,

But iron dug from central gloom,
    And heated hot with burning fears,
    And dipt in baths of hissing tears,
And batter'd with the shocks of doom

To shape and use. Arise and fly
    The reeling Faun, the sensual feast ;
    Move upward, working out the beast,
And let the ape and tiger die.

From ALFRED, LORD TENNYSON, *In Memoriam*
A. H. H. (1850)

SCIENCE AND PROGRESS RECONSIDERED

GONE the cry of 'Forward, Forward,' lost within a growing
    gloom ;
Lost, or only heard in silence from the silence of a tomb.

Half the marvels of my morning, triumphs over time and
    space,
Staled by frequence, shrunk by usage into commonest
    commonplace !

'Forward' rang the voices then, and of the many mine was
    one.
Let us hush this cry of 'Forward' till ten thousand years have
    gone.

.   .   .   .   .

Forward, backward, backward, forward, in the immeasurable
    sea,
Sway'd by vaster ebbs and flows than can be known to you or
    me.

All the suns — are these but symbols of innumerable man,
Man or Mind that sees a shadow of the planner or the plan ?

Is there evil but on earth ? or pain in every peopled sphere ?
Well be grateful for the sounding watchword 'Evolution'
 here,

Evolution ever climbing after some ideal good,
And Reversion ever dragging Evolution in the mud.

What are men that He should heed us ? cried the king of
 sacred song ;
Insects of an hour, that hourly work their brother insect
 wrong,

While the silent Heavens roll, and Suns along their fiery way,
All their planets whirling round them, flash a million miles a
 day.

Many an Æon moulded earth before her highest, man, was
 born,
Many an Æon too may pass when earth is manless and forlorn,

Earth so huge, and yet so bounded — pools of salt, and plots
 of land —
Shallow skin of green and azure — chains of mountain, grains
 of sand !

Only That which made us, meant us to be mightier by and by,
Set the sphere of all the boundless Heavens within the
 human eye,

Sent the shadow of Himself, the boundless, thro' the human
 soul ;
Boundless inward, in the atom, boundless outward, in the
 Whole.

Here is Locksley Hall, my grandson, here the lion-guarded
 gate.
Not to-night in Locksley Hall — to-morrow — you, you
 come so late.

Wreck'd — your train — or all but wreck'd ? a shatter'd
    wheel ? a vicious boy !
Good, this forward, you that preach it, is it well to wish you
    joy ?

Is it well that while we range with Science, glorying in the
    Time,
City children soak and blacken soul and sense in city slime ?

There among the glooming alleys Progress halts on palsied
    feet,
Crime and hunger cast our maidens by the thousand on the
    street.

There the Master scrimps his haggard sempstress of her daily
    bread,
There a single sordid attic holds the living and the dead.

There the smouldering fire of fever creeps across the rotted
    floor,
And the crowded couch of incest in the warrens of the poor.

Nay, your pardon, cry your 'forward,' yours are hope and
    youth, but I —
Eighty winters leave the dog too lame to follow with the cry,

Lame and old, and past his time, and passing now into the
    night ;
Yet I would the rising race were half as eager for the light.

Light the fading gleam of Even ? light the glimmer of the
    dawn ?
Aged eyes may take the growing glimmer for the gleam
    withdrawn.

Far away beyond her myriad coming changes earth will be
Something other than the wildest modern guess of you and
    me.

Alfred, Lord Tennyson

Earth may reach her earthly-worst, or if she gain her earthly-
   best,
Would she find her human offspring this ideal man at rest ?

Forward then, but still remember how the course of Time
   will swerve,
Crook and turn upon itself in many a backward streaming
   curve.

.   .   .   .   .

Yonder lies our young sea-village — Art and Grace are less
   and less :
Science grows and Beauty dwindles — roofs of slated
   hideousness !

There is one old Hostel left us where they swing the Locksley
   shield,
Till the peasant cow shall butt the 'Lion passant' from his
   field.

Poor old Heraldry, poor old History, poor old Poetry,
   passing hence,
In the common deluge drowning old political common-
   sense !

Poor old voice of eighty crying after voices that have fled !
All I loved are vanish'd voices, all my steps are on the
   dead.

All the world is ghost to me, and as the phantom dis-
   appears,
Forward far and far from here is all the hope of eighty
   years.

From ALFRED, LORD TENNYSON, *Locksley Hall Sixty
Years After* (1886)

THE STETHOSCOPE SONG
A Professional Ballad

THERE was a young man in Boston town,
　　He bought him a STETHOSCOPE nice and new,
All mounted and finished and polished down,
　　With an ivory cap and a stopper too.

It happened a spider within did crawl,
　　And spun him a web of ample size,
Wherein there chanced one day to fall
　　A couple of very imprudent flies.

The first was a bottle-fly, big and blue,
　　The second was smaller, and thin and long ;
So there was a concert between the two,
　　Like an octave flute and a tavern gong.

Now being from Paris but recently,
　　This fine young man would show his skill ;
And so they gave him, his hand to try,
　　A hospital patient extremely ill.

Some said that his *liver* was short of *bile*,
　　And some that his *heart* was over size,
While some kept arguing all the while
　　He was crammed with *tubercles* up to his eyes.

This fine young man then up stepped he,
　　And all the doctors made a pause ;
Said he, — The man must die, you see,
　　By the fifty-seventh of Louis's laws.

But since the case is a desperate one,
　　To explore his chest it may be well ;
For if he should die and it were not done,
　　You know the *autopsy* would not tell.

Then out his stethoscope he took,
    And on it placed his curious ear ;
Mon Dieu ! said he, with a knowing look,
    Why here is a sound that's mighty queer !

The *bourdonnement* is very clear, —
    Amphoric buzzing, as I'm alive !
Five doctors took their turn to hear ;
    Amphoric buzzing, said all the five.

There's *empyema* beyond a doubt ;
    We'll plunge a *trocar* in his side. —
The diagnosis was made out,
    They tapped the patient ; so he died.

Now such as hate new-fashioned toys
    Began to look extremely glum ;
They said that *rattles* were made for boys,
    And vowed that his *buzzing* was all a hum.

There was an old lady had long been sick,
    And what was the matter none did know :
Her pulse was slow, though her tongue was quick ;
    To her this knowing youth must go.

So there the nice old lady sat,
    With phials and boxes all in a row ;
She asked the young doctor what he was at,
    To thump her and tumble her ruffles so.

Now, when the stethoscope came out,
    The flies began to buzz and whiz ; —
O ho ! the matter is clear, no doubt ;
    An *aneurism* there plainly is.

The *bruit de râpe* and the *bruit de scie*
    And the *bruit de diable* are all combined ;
How happy Bouillaud would be,
    If he a case like this could find !

Now, when the neighbouring doctors found
  A case so rare had been descried,
They every day her ribs did pound
  In squads of twenty; so she died.

Then six young damsels, slight and frail,
  Received this kind young doctor's cares;
They all were getting slim and pale,
  And short of breath on mounting stairs.

They all made rhymes with 'sighs' and 'skies',
  And loathed their puddings and buttered rolls,
And dieted, much to their friends' surprise,
  On pickles and pencils and chalk and coals.

So fast their little hearts did bound,
  The frightened insects buzzed the more;
So over all their chests he found
  The *râle sifflant*, and the *râle sonore*.

He shook his head; — there's grave disease —
  I greatly fear you all must die;
A slight *post-mortem*, if you please,
  Surviving friends would gratify.

The six young damsels wept aloud,
  Which so prevailed on six young men,
That each his honest love avowed,
  Whereat they all got well again.

This poor young man was all aghast;
  The price of stethoscopes came down;
And so he was reduced at last
  To practise in a country town.

The doctors being very sore,
  A stethoscope they did devise,
That had a rammer to clear the bore,
  With a knob at the end to kill the flies.

Now use your ears, all you that can,
    But don't forget to mind your eyes,
Or you may be cheated, like this young man,
    By a couple of silly, abnormal flies.

            OLIVER WENDELL HOLMES, *Poems*, 2nd ed., 1849

RAILWAYS. 1846

'No poetry in Railways!' foolish thought
Of a dull brain, to no fine music wrought.
By mammon dazzled, though the people prize
The gold alone, yet shall not we despise
The triumphs of our time, or fail to see
Of pregnant mind the fruitful progeny
Ushering the daylight of the world's new morn.
Look up, ye doubters, be no more forlorn ! —
Smooth your rough brows, ye little wise : rejoice,
Ye who despond : and with exulting voice
Salute, ye earnest spirits of our time,
The young Improvement ripening to her prime,
Who, in the fulness of her genial youth,
Prepares the way for Liberty and Truth,
And breaks the barriers that, since earth began,
Have made mankind the enemy of man.

    Lay down your rails, ye nations, near and far —
Yoke your full trains to Steam's triumphal car ;
Link town to town ; unite in iron bands
The long-estranged and oft-embattled lands.
Peace, mild-eyed seraph — Knowledge, light divine,
Shall send their messengers by every line.
Men, join'd in amity, shall wonder long
That Hate had power to lead their fathers wrong ;
Or that false Glory lured their hearts astray,
And made it virtuous and sublime to slay.

Blessings on science ! When the earth seem'd old,
When Faith grew doting, and the Reason cold,
'Twas she discover'd that the world was young,
And taught a language to its lisping tongue :
'Twas she disclosed a future to its view,
And made old knowledge pale before the new.

Blessings on Science ! In her dawning hour
Faith knit her brow, alarm'd for ancient power ;
Then look'd again upon her face sincere,
Held out her hand, and hail'd her — Sister dear ;
And Reason, free as eagle on the wind,
Swoop'd o'er the fallow meadows of the mind,
And, clear of vision, saw what seed would grow
On the hill slopes, or in the vales below ;
What in the sunny South, or nipping Nord,
And from her talons dropp'd it as she soar'd.

Blessings on Science, and her handmaid Steam !
They make Utopia only half a dream ;
And show the fervent, of capacious souls,
Who watch the ball of Progress as it rolls,
That all as yet completed, or begun,
Is but the dawning that precedes the sun.

CHARLES MACKAY, written 1846

TUBAL CAIN

I

OLD Tubal Cain was a man of might
   In the days when earth was young ;
By the fierce red light of his furnace bright
   The strokes of his hammer rung ;
And he lifted high his brawny hand
   On the iron glowing clear,

144

Till the sparks rush'd out in scarlet showers,
   As he fashion'd the sword and spear.
And he sang — 'Hurra for my handiwork !
   Hurra for the Spear and Sword !
Hurra for the hand that shall wield them well,
   For he shall be King and Lord !'

2

To Tubal Cain came many a one,
   As he wrought by his roaring fire,
And each one pray'd for a strong steel blade
   As the crown of his desire ;
And he made them weapons sharp and strong,
   Till they shouted loud for glee,
And gave him gifts of pearls and gold,
   And spoils of the forest free.
And they sang — 'Hurra for Tubal Cain,
   Who hath given us strength anew !
Hurra for the smith, hurra for the fire,
   And hurra for the metal true !'

3

But a sudden change came o'er his heart
   Ere the setting of the sun,
And Tubal Cain was fill'd with pain
   For the evil he had done ;
He saw that men, with rage and hate,
   Made war upon their kind,
That the land was red with the blood they shed
   In their lust for carnage, blind.
And he said — 'Alas ! that ever I made,
   Or that skill of mine should plan,
The spear and the sword for men whose joy
   Is to slay their fellow-man !'

4

And for many a day old Tubal Cain
   Sat brooding o'er his woe ;

And his hand forbore to smite the ore,
  And his furnace smoulder'd low.
But he rose at last with a cheerful face,
  And a bright courageous eye,
And bared his strong right arm for work,
  While the quick flames mounted high.
And he sang — 'Hurra for my handiwork!'
  And the red sparks lit the air;
'Not alone for the blade was the bright steel made;'
  And he fashion'd the First Ploughshare!

5

And men, taught wisdom from the Past,
  In friendship join'd their hands,
Hung the sword in the hall, the spear on the wall,
  And plough'd the willing lands;
And sang — 'Hurra for Tubal Cain!
  Our staunch good friend is he;
And for the ploughshare and the plough
  To him our praise shall be.
But while Oppression lifts its head,
  Or a tyrant would be lord,
Though we may thank him for the Plough,
  We'll not forget the Sword!'

CHARLES MACKAY, written *c.* 1850

THE ASTRONOMER

I

UPON thy lofty tower,
  O lonely Sage,
Reading at midnight hour
  Heaven's awful page!
Thine art can poise the sun
  In balance true,

And countless worlds that run
 Beyond our view.
Thou scannest with clear eyes
 The azure cope ;
To thee the galaxies
 Their secrets ope ;
Thou know'st the track sublime
 Of every star ;
Space infinite, and Time,
 Thy problems are.
O Sage ! whose mental span
 Thus grasps the sky,
How great the soul of man
 That soars so high !

2

But yet thou canst not guess,
 With all thy skill,
What seas of happiness
 My bosom fill.
Thou canst not track the woe,
 The hope, the faith,
That prompt the ebb and flow
 Of my poor breath.
Outspeeding with thy thought
 The solar ray,
Thou canst not, knowledge-fraught,
 Discern my way.
My love — its depth and height, —
 Thou canst not sound ;
Nor of my guilt's dark night
 Pierce the profound.
O student of the sky
 My pride departs ;
Worlds undiscover'd lie
 In both our hearts !

CHARLES MACKAY, *Songs for Music* (1856)

WHEN I HEARD THE LEARN'D ASTRONOMER

WHEN I heard the learn'd astronomer,
When the proofs, the figures, were ranged in columns before
    me,
When I was shown the charts and diagrams, to add, divide,
    and measure them,
When I sitting heard the astronomer where he lectured with
    much applause in the lecture-room,
How soon unaccountable I became tired and sick,
Till rising and gliding out I wander'd off by myself,
In the mystical moist night-air, and from time to time,
Look'd up in perfect silence at the stars.

WALT WHITMAN, written 1865

TO A LOCOMOTIVE IN WINTER

THEE for my recitative,
Thee in the driving storm even as now, the snow, the winter-
    day declining,
Thee in thy panoply, thy measur'd dual throbbing and thy
    beat convulsive,
Thy black cylindric body, golden brass and silvery steel,
Thy ponderous side-bars, parallel and connecting rods,
    gyrating, shuttling at thy sides,
Thy metrical, now swelling pant and roar, now tapering in
    the distance,
Thy great protruding head-light fix'd in front,
Thy long, pale, floating vapor-pennants, tinged with delicate
    purple,
The dense and murky clouds out-belching from thy smoke-
    stack,
Thy knitted frame, thy springs and valves, the tremulous
    twinkle of thy wheels,

Thy train of cars behind, obedient, merrily following,
Through gale or calm, now swift, now slack, yet steadily
    careering ;
Type of the modern — emblem of motion and power —
    pulse of the continent,
For once come serve the Muse and merge in verse, even as
    here I see thee,
With storm and buffeting gusts of wind and falling snow,
By day thy warning ringing bell to sound its notes,
By night thy silent signal lamps to swing.

Fierce-throated beauty !
Roll through my chant with all thy lawless music, thy
    swinging lamps at night,
Thy madly-whistled laughter, echoing, rumbling like an
    earthquake, rousing all,
Law of thyself complete, thine own track firmly holding,
(No sweetness debonair of tearful harp or glib piano thine,)
Thy trills of shrieks by rocks and hills return'd,
Launch'd o'er the prairies wide, across the lakes,
To the free skies unpent and glad and strong.

WALT WHITMAN, written 1876

THE MATHEMATICIAN IN LOVE

1

A MATHEMATICIAN fell madly in love
    With a lady, young, handsome, and charming :
By angles and ratios harmonic he strove
Her curves and proportions all faultless to prove.
    As he scrawled hieroglyphics alarming.

2

He measured with care, from the ends of a base,
    The arcs which her features subtended :

149

Then he framed transcendental equations, to trace
The flowing outlines of her figure and face,
   And thought the result very splendid.

3

He studied (since music has charms for the fair)
   The theory of fiddles and whistles, —
Then composed, by acoustic equations, an air,
Which, when 'twas performed, made the lady's long hair
   Stand on end, like a porcupine's bristles.

4

The lady loved dancing : — he therefore applied,
   To the polka and waltz, an equation ;
But when to rotate on his axis he tried,
His centre of gravity swayed to one side,
   And he fell, by the earth's gravitation.

5

No doubts of the fate of his suit made him pause,
   For he proved, to his own satisfaction,
That the fair one returned his affection ; — 'because,
'As every one knows, by mechanical laws,
   'Re-action is equal to action.'

6

'Let x denote beauty, — y, manners well-bred, —
   'z, Fortune, — (this last is essential), —
'Let L stand for love' — our philosopher said, —
'Then L is a function of x, y, and z,
   'Of the kind which is known as potential.'

7

'Now integrate L with respect to $d\,t$,
   '(t Standing for time and persuasion) ;
'Then, between proper limits, 'tis easy to see,
'The definite integral *Marriage* must be : —
   '(A very concise demonstration).'

8

Said he — 'If the wandering course of the moon
  'By Algebra can be predicted,
'The female affections must yield to it soon' —
— But the lady ran off with a dashing dragoon,
  And left him amazed and afflicted.

W. J. M. RANKINE, *Songs and Fables* (1874)

MEDITATION UNDER STARS

WHAT links are ours with orbs that are
    So resolutely far :
The solitary asks, and they
Give radiance as from a shield :
    Still at the death of day,
    The seen, the unrevealed.
    Implacable they shine
To us who would of Life obtain
An answer for the life we strain
    To nourish with one sign.
Nor can imagination throw
The penetrative shaft : we pass
The breath of thought, who would divine
    If haply they may grow
As Earth ; have our desire to know ;
If life comes there to grain from grass,
And flowers like ours of toil and pain ;
    Has passion to beat bar,
    Win space from cleaving brain ;
    The mystic link attain,
    Whereby star holds on star.

Those visible immortals beam
    Allurement to the dream :

Ireful at human hungers brook
  No question in the look.
For ever virgin to our sense,
Remote they wane to gaze intense :
Prolong it, and in ruthlessness they smite
The beating heart behind the ball of sight :
   Till we conceive their heavens hoar,
   Those lights they raise but sparkles frore,
And Earth, our bloom-warm Earth, a shuddering prey
To that frigidity of brainless ray.

Yet space is given for breath of thought
Beyond our bounds when musing : more
When to that musing love is brought,
And love is asked of love's wherefore.
'Tis Earth's, her gift ; else have we nought :
Her gift, her secret, here our tie.
And not with her and yonder sky ?
Bethink you : were it Earth alone
Breeds love, would not her region be
   The sole delight and throne
   Of generous Deity ?

   To deeper than this ball of sight
Appeal the lustrous people of the night.
Fronting yon shoreless, sown with fiery sails,
   It is our ravenous that quails,
Flesh by its craven thirsts and fears distraught.
     The spirit leaps alight,
     Doubts not in them is he,
The binder of his sheaves, the sane, the right :
Of magnitude to magnitude is wrought,
To feel it large of the great life they hold :
In them to come, or vaster intervolved,
The issues known in us, our unsolved solved :
That there with toil Life climbs the self-same Tree,
Whose roots enrichment have from ripeness dropped.
So may we read and little find them cold :

George Meredith

Let it but be the lord of Mind to guide
Our eyes ; no branch of Reason's growing lopped ;
Nor dreaming on a dream ; but fortified
By day to penetrate black midnight ; see,
Hear, feel, outside the senses ; even that we,
The specks of dust upon a mound of mould,
We who reflect those rays, though low our place,
   To them are lastingly allied.

So may we read, and little find them cold :
Not frosty lamps illumining dead space,
Not distant aliens, not senseless Powers.
The fire is in them whereof we are born ;
The music of their motion may be ours.
Spirit shall deem them beckoning Earth and voiced
Sisterly to her, in her beams rejoiced.
Of love, the grand impulsion, we behold
   The love that lends her grace
   Among the starry fold.
Then at new flood of customary morn,
   Look at her through her showers,
   Her mists, her streaming gold,
A wonder edges the familiar face :
She wears no more that robe of printed hours ;
Half strange seems Earth, and sweeter than her flowers.

GEORGE MEREDITH, *A Reading of Earth* (1888)

TO THE PLIOCENE SKULL

(*A Geological Address*)

'SPEAK, O man, less recent ! Fragmentary fossil !
Primal pioneer of pliocene formation,
Hid in lowest drifts below the earliest stratum
      Of volcanic tufa !

'Older than the beasts, the oldest Palæotherium ;
Older than the trees, the oldest Cryptogami ;
Older than the hills, those infantile eruptions
      Of earth's epidermis !

'Eo — Mio — Plio — whatsoe'er the "cene" was
That those vacant sockets filled with awe and wonder, —
Whether shores Devonian or Silurian beaches, —
      Tell us thy strange story !

'Or has the professor slightly antedated
By some thousand years thy advent on this planet,
Giving thee an air that's somewhat better fitted
      For cold-blooded creatures ?

'Wert thou true spectator of that mighty forest
When above thy head the stately Sigillaria
Reared its columned trunks in that remote and distant
      Carboniferous epoch ?

'Tell us of that scene, — the dim and watery woodland,
Songless, silent, hushed, with never bird or insect,
Veiled with spreading fronds and screened with tall club-
      mosses,
      Lycopodiacea, —

'When beside thee walked the solemn Plesiosaurus,
And around thee crept the festive Ichthyosaurus,
While from time to time above thee flew and circled
      Cheerful Pterodactyls.

'Tell us of thy food, — those half-marine refections,
Crinoids on the shell and Brachipods *au natural*, —
Cuttlefish to which the *pieuvre* of Victor Hugo
      Seems a periwinkle.

'Speak, thou awful vestige of the earth's creation, —
Solitary fragment of remains organic !

Tell the wondrous secret of thy past existence, —
    Speak ! thou oldest primate !'

Even as I gazed, a thrill of the maxilla,
And a lateral movement of the condyloid process,
With post-pliocene sounds of healthy mastication,
    Ground the teeth together.

And, from that imperfect dental exhibition,
Stained with express juices of the weed Nicotian,
Came these hollow accents, blent with softer murmurs
    Of expectoration :

'Which my name is Bowers, and my crust was busted
Falling down a shaft in Calaveras County,
But I'd take it kindly if you'd send the pieces
    Home to old Missouri !'

Francis Bret Harte, written 1866

A GEOLOGICAL MADRIGAL

(*Parody — William Shenstone*)

I have found out a gift for my fair ;
    I know where the fossils abound,
Where the footprints of *Aves* declare
    The birds that once walked on the ground ;
Oh, come, and — in technical speech —
    We'll walk this Devonian shore,
Or on some Silurian beach
    We'll wander, my love, evermore.

I will show thee the sinuous track
    By the slow-moving annelid made,
Or the Trilobite that, farther back,
    In the old Potsdam sandstone was laid ;

Thou shalt see, in his Jurassic tomb,
 The Plesiosaurus embalmed ;
In his Oolitic prime and his bloom,
 Iguanodon safe and unharmed !

You wished — I remember it well,
 And I loved you the more for that wish —
For a perfect cystedian shell
 And a *whole* holocephalic fish.
And oh, if Earth's strata contains
 In its lowest Silurian drift,
Or palæozoic remains
 The same, — 'tis your lover's free gift !

Then come, love, and never say nay,
 But calm all your maidenly fears ;
We'll note, love, in one summer's day
 The record of millions of years ;
And though the Darwinian plan
 Your sensitive feelings may shock,
We'll find the beginning of man, —
 Our fossil ancestors, in rock !

FRANCIS BRET HARTE, written 1867

AT A LUNAR ECLIPSE

THY shadow, Earth, from Pole to Central Sea,
Now steals along upon the Moon's meek shine
In even monochrome and curving line
Of imperturbable serenity.

How shall I link such sun-cast symmetry
With the torn troubled form I know as thine,
That profile, placid as a brow divine,
With continents of moil and misery ?

And can immense Mortality but throw
So small a shade, and Heaven's high human scheme
Be hemmed within the coasts yon arc implies ?

Is such the stellar gauge of earthly show,
Nation at war with nation, brains that teem,
Heroes, and women fairer than the skies ?

THOMAS HARDY, *Poems of the Past
and the Present* (1901)

HEREDITY

I AM the family face ;
Flesh perishes, I live on,
Projecting trait and trace
Through time to times anon,
And leaping from place to place
Over oblivion.

The years-heired feature that can
In curve and voice and eye
Despise the human span
Of durance — that is I ;
The eternal thing in man,
That heeds no call to die.

THOMAS HARDY, *Moments of Vision and
Miscellaneous Verses* (1917)

A BALLADE OF EVOLUTION

IN the mud of the Cambrian main
   Did our earliest ancestor dive :
From a shapeless albuminous grain
   We mortals our being derive.

He could split himself up into five,
　　Or roll himself round like a ball ;
For the fittest will always survive,
　　While the weakliest go to the wall.

As an active ascidian again
　　Fresh forms he began to contrive,
Till he grew to a fish with a brain,
　　And brought forth a mammal alive.
With his rivals he next had to strive
　　To woo him a mate and a thrall ;
So the handsomest managed to wive,
　　While the ugliest went to the wall.

At length as an ape he was fain
　　The nuts of the forest to rive,
Till he took to the low-lying plain,
　　And proceeded his fellows to knive.
Thus did cannibal men first arrive
　　One another to swallow and maul :
And the strongest continued to thrive,
　　While the weakliest went to the wall.

ENVOY

Prince, in our civilised hive,
　　Now money's the measure of all ;
And the wealthy in coaches can drive,
　　While the needier go to the wall.

　　　　　　GRANT ALLEN, *The Lower Slopes* (1894)

BALLAD OF THE ICHTHYOSAURUS

I ABIDE in a goodly Museum,
　　Frequented by sages profound :
'Tis a kind of strange mausoleum,
　　Where the beasts that have vanished abound.

May Kendall

There's a bird of the ages Triassic,
    With his antediluvian beak,
And many a reptile Jurassic,
    And many a monster antique.

Ere Man was developed, our brother,
    We swam and we ducked and we dived,
And we dined, as a rule, on each other —
    What matter, the toughest survived.
Our paddles were fins, and they bore us
    Through water : in air we could fly ;
But the brain of the Ichthyosaurus
    Was never a match for his eye.

Geologists, active and eager,
    Its excellence hasten to own,
And praise, with no eulogy meagre,
    The eye that is plated with bone.
'See how, with unerring precision,
    His prey through the wave he could spy.
Oh, wonderful organ of vision,
    Gigantic and beautiful Eye !'

Then I listen in gloomy dejection,
    I gaze, and I wish I could weep ;
For what is mere visual perfection
    To Intellect subtle and deep ?
A loftier goal is before us,
    For higher endowments we sigh.
But the brain of the Ichthyosaurus
    Was never a patch on his eye !

It owned no supreme constitution,
    Was shallow, and simple, and plain,
While mark but the fair convolution
    And size of the Aryan brain.

'Tis furnished for School Board inspections,
  And garnished for taking degrees,
And bulging in many directions,
  As every phrenologist sees.

Sometimes it explodes at high pressure
  Of some overwhelming demand,
But plied in unmerciful measure
  'Tis wonderful what it will stand !
In college, in cottage, in mansion,
  Bear witness, the girls and the boys,
How great are its powers of expansion,
  How very peculiar its joys !

Oh Brain that is bulgy with learning,
  Oh wisdom of women and men,
Oh Maids for a First that are yearning,
  Oh youths that are lectured by Wren !
You're acquainted with Pisces and Taurus,
  And all sorts of beasts in the sky,
But the brain of the Ichthyosaurus
  Was never so good as his eye !

Reconstructed by Darwin or Owen,
  We dwell in sweet Bloomsbury's halls,
But we couldn't have passed Little go in
  The Schools, we'd have floundered in Smalls !
Though so cleverly people restore us,
  We are bound to confess with a sigh
That the brain of the Ichthyosaurus
  Was *never* so good as his eye !

MAY KENDALL (MRS. ANDREW LANG),
Dreams to Sell (1887)

May Kendall

'TAKING LONG VIEWS'

His locks were wild, and wild his eye,
  Furrowed his brow with anxious thought.
Musing I asked him : 'Tell me why
  You look thus vacant and distraught ?'
Sadly he gazed into my face :
  He said, 'I have no respite, none !
Oh, shall we wander into space
  Or fall into the sun ?

'Astronomers I've sought in tears,
  And ah, 'tis terribly remiss
That after all these anxious years
  They cannot even tell us this !
Though each man seems to prove his case,
  Each contradicts the other one,
And — *do* we wander into space
  Or fall into the sun ?'

'Comfort !' I said, 'I can't discern
  The nature of our planet's end,
Nor should I greatly care to learn.
  We've many aeons left, my friend !
Whether we last from age to age
  A frozen ball, or turn to flame,
To me, at this inspiring stage,
  Is very much the same.

'Observe Humanity's advance,
  And Evolution's giant strides !
Remark on what a smooth expanse
  The nation's barque at anchor rides !
The march of Intellect retrace.'
  He moaned : 'I don't care what we've done.
Oh, shall we wander into space
  Or fall into the sun ?

'If we should fall, you understand,
  Such heat the crash would generate
The solar system might expand
  Into its primal gaseous state.
It would be awkward, I maintain,
  The same old cycle to renew ;
For once let things come round again,
  And *we* should come round too !'

I cried : 'The prophecy forbear !
  Of finite woes we have enough.
What, travel through the old despair,
  Experience the old rebuff !
I'd rather haunt the void Afar
  For endless ages, would rejoice
To be a harmless frozen star,
  If I might have my choice !'

He gazed at me with aspect strange.
  He only said : 'How would it be
If this poor planet should derange
  The solar system's equity ;
If when the sun our planet met
  The sun himself began to fall,
Another system to upset,
  And so on through them all ?'

'Peace, peace !' I said. 'However dark
  The destiny the aeons bear,
You won't be here the wreck to mark.'
  He cried : '*That* causes my despair.
I want to know what will take place,
  I want to see what will be done.
Oh, shall we wander into space
  Or fall into the sun ?'

MAY KENDALL (MRS. ANDREW LANG),
Dreams to Sell (1887)

THE CONQUERING MACHINE

You say that 'Evolution's blind,
   Her purpose unforeseen,' —
Nay, for as types she leaves behind,
She keeps for ever in her mind
   The Conquering Machine!

Even now, — O future years of grace,
   The prophecy fulfil!
Our hearts the dawning influence trace,
The 'nerve of steel' we try to brace,
   Or bend 'the iron will.'

Now, to the eye of faith displayed,
   The coming form is seen;
In every office, every trade,
I watch, in human garb arrayed,
   The Conquering Machine!

In the dim watches of the night
   I see the portent rise,
A creature of unearthly might,
Irradiate with electric light,
   And justly focussed eyes!

By careful Evolution planned
   With many a gliding wheel,
To warn, to comfort, to command,
To fly, to drive a four-in-hand,
   Or dance a Highland reel!

Volition vain will fret no more
   The Automatic Soul,
Emotion then will fail to score,
While reflex action takes the floor,
   And dominates the whole!

Machines no conscience will neglect,
   No scruples will endure,
For conscience, in that realm correct
Of automatic intellect,
   Will be a sinecure !

Ay, driven no more by passion's gale,
   Nor impulse unforeseen,
Humanity shall faint and fail,
And on her ruins will prevail
   The Conquering Machine !

Responsibility begone !
   Let Freedom's flag be furled ;
Oh, coming ages, hasten on,
And bring the true Automaton,
   The monarch of the world.

MAY KENDALL (MRS. ANDREW LANG),
Dreams to Sell (1887)

SUCCESS IN MALARIA RESEARCH

THIS day relenting God
   Hath placed within my hand
A wondrous thing ; and God
   Be praised. At his command,

Seeking His secret deeds
   With tears and toiling breath,
I find thy cunning seeds,
   O million-murdering Death.

I know this little thing
   A myriad men will save.
O Death, where is thy sting ?
   Thy victory, O Grave ?

SIR RONALD ROSS, written 1897

Sir Ronald Ross

THE ANNIVERSARY
(*August 20th*, 1917)

Now twenty years ago
  This day we found the thing;
With science and with skill
  We found: then came the sting —
What we with endless labour won
  The thick world scorned;
Not worth a word today —
  Not worth remembering.

O Gorgeous Gardens, Lands
  Of beauty where the Sun
His lordly raiment trails
  All day with light enspun,
We found the death that lurk'd beneath
  Your purple leaves,
We found your secret foe,
  The million-murdering one;

And clapp'd our hands and thought
  Your teeming width would ring
With that great victory — more
  Than battling hosts can bring.
Ah, well — men laugh'd. The years have pass'd;
  The world is cold —
Some million lives a year,
  Not worth remembering!

Ascended from below
  Men still remain too small;
With belly-wisdom big
  They fight and bite and bawl,
These larval angels! — but when true
  Achievement comes —
A trifling doctor's matter —
  No consequence at all.

                    SIR RONALD ROSS, written 1917

165

THE TURBINE

LOOK at her — there she sits upon her throne
As ladylike and quiet as a nun !
But if you cross her — whew ! her thunderbolts
Will shake the earth ! She's proud as any queen,
The beauty — knows her royal business too,
To light the world, and does it night by night
When her gay lord, the sun, gives up his job.
I am her slave ; I wake and watch and run
From dark till dawn beside her. All the while
She hums there softly, purring with delight
Because men bring the riches of the earth
To feed her hungry fires. I do her will
And dare not disobey, for her right hand
Is power, her left is terror, and her anger
Is havoc. Look — if I but lay a wire
Across the terminals of yonder switch
She'll burst her windings, rip her casings off,
And shriek till envious Hell shoots up its flames,
Shattering her very throne. And all her people,
The laboring, trampling, dreaming crowds out there —
Fools and the wise who look to her for light —
Will walk in darkness through the liquid night,
Submerged.
        Sometimes I wonder why she stoops
To be my friend — oh yes, who talks to me
And sings away my loneliness ; my friend,
Though I am trivial and she sublime.
Hard-hearted ? — No, tender and pitiful,
As all the great are. Every arrogant grief
She comforts quietly, and all my joys
Dance to her measures through the tolerant night.
She talks to me, tells me her troubles too,
Just as I tell her mine. Perhaps she feels
An ache deep down — that agonizing stab
Of grit grating her bearings ; then her voice

Changes its tune, it wails and calls to me
To soothe her anguish, and I run, her slave,
Probe like a surgeon and relieve the pain.

We have our jokes too, little mockeries
That no one else in all the swarming world
Would see the point of. She will laugh at me
To show her power : maybe her carbon packings
Leak steam, and I run madly back and forth
To keep the infernal fiends from breaking loose —
Suddenly she will throttle them herself
And chuckle softly, far above me there,
At my alarms.
    But there are times, you know,
When my turn comes ; her slave can be her master,
Conquering her he serves. For she's a woman,
Gets bored there on her throne, tired of herself,
Tingles with power that turns to wantonness.
Suddenly something's wrong — she laughs at me,
Bedevils the frail wires with some mad caress
That thrills blind space, calls down ten thousand
  lightnings
To shatter her world and set her spirit free.
Then with this puny hand, swift as her threat,
Must I beat back the chaos, hold in leash
Destructive furies, rescue her — even her —
From the fierce rashness of her truant mood,
And make me lord of far and near a moment,
Startling the mystery. Last night I did it —
Alone here with my hand upon her heart
I faced the mounting fiends and whipped them down ;
And never a wink from the long file of lamps
Betrayed her to the world.
     So there she sits,
Mounted on all the ages, at the peak
Of time. The first man dreamed of light, and dug
The sodden ignorance away, and cursed
The darkness ; young primeval races dragged

Foundation stones, and piled into the void
Rage and desire ; the Greek mounted and sang
Promethean songs and lit a signal fire ;
The Roman bent his iron will to forge
Deep furnaces ; slow epochs riveted
With hope the secret chambers : till at last
We, you and I, this living age of ours,
A new-winged Mercury, out of the skies
Filch the wild spirit of light, and chain him there
To do her will forever.
                              Look, my friend,
Behold a sign ! What is this crystal sphere —
This little bulb of glass I lightly lift,
This iridescent bubble a child might blow
Out of its brazen pipe to hold the sun —
What strange toy is it ? In my hand it lies
Cold and inert, its puny artery —
That curling cobweb film — ashen and dead.
But see — a twist or two — let it but touch
The hem, far trailing, of my lady's robe,
And quick, the burning life-blood of the stars
Leaps to its heart, that glows against the dark,
Kindling the world.
                              Even so I touch her garment,
Her servant through the quiet night ; and thus
I lay my hand upon the Pleiades
And feel their throb of fire. Grandly she gives
To me unworthy ; woman inscrutable,
Scatters her splendors through my darkness, leads me
Far out into the workshop of the worlds.
There I can feel those infinite energies
Our little earth just gnaws at through the ether,
And see the light our sunshine hides. Out there
Close to the heart of life I am at peace.

                              HARRIET MONROE, written 1910

Harriet Monroe

THE GRAF ZEPPELIN

'SILVERY slick it slithered through the air,'
My driver said, 'and down on earth the crowd —
The whole damn town — stretched up its eyes to stare.
The fella next me was dumb — "take off your hat
And wave," I says, "and let your voice out loud ;
When a mere human does a thing like that
He's got a big cheer coming to him," I says.
You bet he waved — he was kinda in a daze.

'Around the world in a gas-bag — up in the sky —
Between you and the lightning only a bit of leather —
I'll say it's wonderful ! There, not so high,
The big thing slid along through the sunny weather
With airplanes scooting around like little birds.
'Twas a grand sight — you can't tell it in words !
It's great to be alive today, you know,
With all these wonders going on.'

                              And so
We reached the station and I took my train,
Humming his phrases like a song's refrain :

You can't tell it in words !
It's great to be alive,
With wonders going on !
It's great to be alive !

HARRIET MONROE, *Chosen Poems* (1935)

THE MAN OF SCIENCE SPEAKS

THROW your little dreams away,
Scrap philosophies and creeds.
Can your vision of truth climb higher
Than our calculation leads ?

169

While you speculate in vain,
  Making little gods, forsooth,
We fathom infinities —
  Mathematics *is* the truth.

You put limits of your own
  On the illimitable power —
We explore immensities
  Beyond our little place and hour.

With small beliefs or coward doubts
  You lean upon the rotted past.
We neither believe nor doubt — we know ;
  Our rock of faith is anchored fast.

Yesterday's failure is today
  The take-off for tomorrow's goal.
We watch you trembling while we win
  New spaces for the searching soul.

You dream the same old idle dreams,
  You move not in the drift of years.
We count the paces of the stars,
  We hear the singing of the spheres.

HARRIET MONROE, Chosen Poems (1935)

NEW BALLAD OF SIR PATRICK SPENS

(Parody — Old Border Ballad)

THE King sits in Dunfermline toun
  Drinking the blude-red wine :
'O wha will rear me an equilateral triangle
  Upon a given straight line ?'

O up and spake an eldern knight,
   Sat at the King's right knee —
'Of a' the clerks by Granta side
   Sir Patrick bears the gree.

'''Tis he was taught by the Tod-huntére
   Tho' not at the tod-hunting ;
Yet gif that he be given a line,
   He'll do as brave a thing.'

Our King has written a braid letter
   To Cambrigge or thereby,
And there it found Sir Patrick Spens
   Evaluating π.

He hadna warked his quotient
   A point but barely three,
There stepped to him a little foot-page
   And louted on his knee.

The first word that Sir Patrick read,
   ' *Plus* x ' was a' he said :
The neist word that Sir Patrick read,
   'Twas ' *plus* expenses paid.'

The last word that Sir Patrick read,
   The tear blinded his e'e :
'The pound I most admire is not
   In Scottish currencie.'

Stately stepped he east the wa',
   And stately stepped he north :
He fetched a compass frae his ha'
   And stood beside the Forth.

Then gurly grew the waves o' Forth,
   And gurlier by-and-by —
'O never yet was sic a storm,
   Yet it isna sic as I !'

Syne he has crost the Firth o' Forth
  Until Dunfermline toun ;
And tho' he came with a kittle wame
  Fu' low he louted doun.

'A line, a line, a gude straight line,
  O King, purvey me quick !
And see it be of thilka kind
  That's neither braid nor thick.'

'Nor thick nor braid ?' King Jamie said,
  'I'll eat my gude hat-band
If arra line as ye define
  Be found in our Scotland.'

'Tho' there be nane in a' thy rule,
  It sall be ruled by me ;'
And lichtly with his little pencil
  He's ruled the line A B.

Stately stepped he east the wa',
  And stately stepped he west ;
'Ye touch the button,' Sir Patrick said,
  'And I sall do the rest.'

And he has set his compass foot
  Until the centre A,
From A to B he's stretched it oot —
  'Ye Scottish carles, give way !'

Syne he has moved his compass foot
  Until the centre B,
From B to A he's stretched it oot,
  And drawn it viz-a-vee.

The tane circle was B C D,
  And A C E the tither :
'I rede ye well,' Sir Patrick said,
  'They interseck ilk ither.

'See here, and where they interseck —
   To wit with yon point C —
Ye'll just obsairve that I conneck
   The twa points A and B.

'And there ye have a little triangle
   As bonny as e'er was seen ;
The whilk is not isosceles,
   Nor yet it is scalene.'

'The proof ! the proof !' King Jamie cried :
   'The how and eke the why !'
Sir Patrick laughed within his beard —
   ''Tis *ex hypothesi* —

'When I ligg'd in my mither's wame,
   I learn'd it frae my mither,
That things was equal to the same,
   Was equal ane to t'ither.

'Sith in the circle first I drew
   The lines B A, B C,
Be radii true, I wit to you
   The baith maun equal be.

'Likewise and in the second circle,
   Whilk I drew widdershins,
It is nae skaith the radii baith,
   A B, A C, be twins.

'And sith of three a pair agree
   That ilk suld equal ane,
By certes they maun equal be
   Ilk unto ilk by-lane.'

'Now by my faith !' King Jamie saith,
   'What *plane* geometrie !
If only Potts had written in Scots,
   How loocid Potts wad be !'

'Now wow's my life !' said Jamie the King,
   And the Scots lords said the same,
For but it was that envious knicht,
   Sir Hughie o' the Graeme.

'Flim-flam, flim-flam !' and 'Ho indeed ?'
   Quod Hughie o' the Graeme ;
''Tis I could better upon my heid
   This prabblin prablem-game.'

Sir Patrick Spens was nothing laith
   When as he heard 'flim-flam,'
But syne he's ta'en a silken claith
   And wiped his diagram.

'Gif my small feat may better'd be,
   Sir Hew, by thy big head,
What I hae done with an A B C
   Do thou with X Y Z.'

Then sairly sairly swore Sir Hew,
   And loudly laucht the King ;
But Sir Patrick tuk the pipes and blew,
   And *played* that eldritch thing !

He's play'd it reel, he's play'd it jig,
   And the baith alternative ;
And he's danced Sir Hew to the Asses' Brigg,
   That's Proposetion Five.

And there they've met, and there they've fet,
   Forenenst the Asses' Brigg,
And waefu', waefu' was the fate
   That gar'd them there to ligg.

For there Sir Patrick's slain Sir Hew,
   And Sir Hew Sir Patrick Spens —
Now was not that a fine to-do
   For Euclid's Elemen's ?

But let us sing Long live the King !
    And his foes the Deil attend 'em :
For he has gotten his little triangle,
    Quod erat faciendum !

> SIR ARTHUR T. QUILLER-COUCH, *From a Cornish*
> *Window* (1906)

M'ANDREW'S HYMN

LORD, Thou hast made this world below the shadow of a
    dream,
An', taught by time, I tak' it so — exceptin' always Steam.
From coupler-flange to spindle-guide I see Thy Hand, O
    God —
Predestination in the stride o' yon connectin'-rod.
John Calvin might ha' forged the same — enorrmous,
    certain, slow —
Ay, wrought it in the furnace-flame — *my* 'Institutio.'
I cannot get my sleep to-night ; old bones are hard to please ;
I'll stand the middle watch up here — alone wi' God an'
    these
My engines, after ninety days o' race an' rack an' strain
Through all the seas of all Thy world, slam-bangin' home
    again.
Slam-bang too much — they knock a wee — the crosshead-
    gibs are loose,
But thirty thousand mile o' sea has gied them fair excuse. . . .
Fine, clear an' dark — a full-draught breeze, wi' Ushant out
    o' sight,
An' Ferguson relievin' Hay. Old girl, ye'll walk to-night !
His wife's at Plymouth. . . . Seventy — One — Two —
    Three since he began —
Three turns for Mistress Ferguson . . . and who's to blame
    the man ?
There's none at any port for me, by drivin' fast or slow,

Since Elsie Campbell went to Thee, Lord, thirty years ago.
(The year the *Sarah Sands* was burned. Oh roads we used to tread,
Fra' Maryhill to Pollokshaws — fra' Govan to Parkhead !)
Not but they're ceevil on the Board. Ye'll hear Sir Kenneth say :
'Good morrn, McAndrew ! Back again ? An' How's your bilge to-day ?'
Miscallin' technicalities but handin' me my chair
To drink Madeira wi' three Earls — the auld Fleet Engineer
That started as a boiler-whelp — when steam and he were low.
I mind the time we used to serve a broken pipe wi' tow !
Ten pound was all the pressure then — Eh ! Eh ! — a man wad drive ;
An' here, our workin' gauges give one hunder sixty-five !
We're creepin' on wi' each new rig — less weight an' larger power ;
There'll be the loco-boiler next an' thirty miles an hour !
Thirty an' more. What I ha' seen since ocean-steam began
Leaves me na doot for the machine : but what about the man ?
The man that counts, wi' all his runs, one million mile o' sea :
Four time the span from earth to moon. . . . How far, O Lord, from Thee
That wast beside him night an' day ? Ye mind my first typhoon ?
It scoughed the skipper on his way to jock wi' the saloon.
Three feet were on the stokehold-floor — just slappin' to an' fro —
An' cast me on a furnace-door. I have the marks to show.
Marks ! I ha' marks o' more than burns — deep in my soul an' black,
An' times like this, when things go smooth, my wickudness comes back.
The sins o' four an' forty years, all up an' down the seas.
Clack an' repeat like valves half-fed. . . . Forgie's our trespasses !

Nights when I'd come on deck to mark, wi' envy in my gaze,
The couples kittlin' in the dark between the funnel-stays ;
Years when I raked the Ports wi' pride to fill my cup o'
    wrong —
Judge not, O Lord, my steps aside at Gay Street in Hong-
    Kong !
Blot out the wastrel hours of mine in sin when I abode —
Jane Harrigan's an' Number Nine, The Reddick an' Grant
    Road !
An' waur than all — my crownin' sin — rank blasphemy an'
    wild.
I was not four and twenty then — Ye wadna judge a child ?
I'd seen the Tropics first that run — new fruit, new smells,
    new air —
How could I tell — blind-fou wi' sun — the Deil was lurkin'
    there ?
By day like playhouse-scenes the shore slid past our sleepy
    eyes ;
By night those soft, lasceevious stars leered from those
    velvet skies,
In port (we used no cargo-steam) I'd daunder down the
    streets —
An ijjit grinnin' in a dream — for shells an' parrakeets,
An' walkin'-sticks o' carved bamboo an' blowfish stuffed an'
    dried —
Fillin' my bunk wi' rubbishry the Chief put overside.
Till, off Sambawa Head, Ye mind, I heard a land-breeze ca',
Milk-warm wi' breath o' spice an' bloom : 'McAndrew,
    come awa' !'
Firm, clear an' low — no haste, no hate — the ghostly
    whisper went,
Just statin' eevidential facts beyon' all argument :
'Your mither's God's a graspin' deil, the shadow o' yoursel',
'Got out o' books by meenisters clean daft on Heaven an'
    Hell.
'They mak' him in the Broomielaw, o' Glasgie cold an' dirt,
'A jealous, pridefu' fetich, lad, that's only strong to hurt.
'Ye'll not go back to Him again an' kiss His red-hot rod,

'But come wi' Us' (Now, who were *They*?) 'an' know the
    Leevin' God,
'That does not kipper souls for sport or break a life in jest,
'But swells the ripenin' cocoanuts an' ripes the woman's
    breast.'
An' there it stopped : cut off : no more ; that quiet, certain
    voice —
For me, six months o' twenty-four, to leave or take at choice.
'Twas on me like a thunderclap — it racked me through an'
    through —
Temptation past the show o' speech, unnameable an' new —
The Sin against the Holy Ghost ? . . . An' under all, our
    screw.

That storm blew by but left behind her anchor-shiftin' swell.
Thou knowest all my heart an' mind, Thou knowest, Lord, I
    fell —
Third on the *Mary Gloster* then, and first that night in Hell !
Yet was Thy Hand beneath my head, about my feet Thy
    Care —
Fra' Deli clear to Torres Strait, the trial o' despair,
But when we touched the Barrier Reef Thy answer to my
    prayer ! . . .
We dared na run that sea by night but lay an' held our fire,
An' I was drowsin' on the hatch — sick — sick wi' doubt an'
    tire :
'*Better the sight of eyes that see than wanderin' o' desire !*'
Ye mind that word ? Clear as our gongs — again, an' once
    again,
When rippin' down through coral-trash ran out our moorin'-
    chain :
An', by Thy Grace, I had the Light to see my duty plain.
Light on the engine-room — no more — bright as our
    carbons burn.
I've lost it since a thousand times, but never past return !

    ·   ·   ·   ·   ·

Obsairve ! Per annum we'll have here two thousand souls
    aboard —

Think not I dare to justify myself before the Lord,
But — average fifteen hunder souls safe-borne fra' port to
    port —
I *am* o' service to my kind. Ye wadna blame the thought?
Maybe they steam from Grace to Wrath — to sin by folly
    led —
It isna mine to judge their path — their lives are on my head.
Mine at the last — when all is done it all comes back to me,
The fault that leaves six thousand ton a log upon the sea.
We'll tak' one stretch — three weeks an' odd by ony road ye
    steer —
Fra' Cape Town east to Wellington — ye need an engineer.
Fail there — ye've time to weld your shaft — ay, eat it, ere
    ye're spoke ;
Or make Kerguelen under sail — three jiggers burned wi'
    smoke !
An' home again — the Rio run : it's no child's play to go
Steamin' to bell for fourteen days o' snow an' floe an' blow.
The bergs like kelpies overside that girn an' turn an' shift
Whaur, grindin' like the Mills o' God, goes by the big South
    drift.
(Hail, Snow and Ice that praise the Lord. I've met them at
    their work,
An' wished we had anither route or they anither kirk.)
Yon's strain, hard strain, o' head an' hand, for though Thy
    Power brings
All skill to naught, Ye'll understand a man must think o'
    things.
Then, at the last, we'll get to port an' hoist their baggage
    clear —
The passengers, wi' gloves an' canes — an' this is what I'll
    hear :
'Well, thank ye for a pleasant voyage. The tender's comin'
    now.'
While I go testin' follower-bolts an' watch the skipper bow.
They've words for every one but me — shake hands wi'
    half the crew,
Except the dour Scots engineer, the man they never knew.

An' yet I like the wark for all we've dam' few pickin's here —
No pension, an' the most we'll earn's four hunder pound a
    year.
Better myself abroad ?   Maybe.   *I'd* sooner starve than sail
Wi' such as call a snifter-rod *ross*. . . . French for nightin-
    gale.
Commeesion on my stores ?   Some do ; but I cannot afford
To lie like stewards wi' patty-pans.   I'm older than the
    Board.
A bonus on the coal I save ?   Ou ay, the Scots are close,
But when I grudge the strength Ye gave I'll grudge their
    food to *those*.
(There's bricks that I might recommend — an' clink the fire-
    bars cruel.
No !   Welsh — Wangarti at the worst — an' damn all patent
    fuel !)
Inventions ?   Ye must stay in port to mak' a patent pay.
My Deeferential Valve-Gear taught me how that business lay.
I blame no chaps wi' clearer heads for aught they make or
    sell.
I found that I could not invent an' look to these as well.
So, wrestled wi' Apollyon — Nah ! — fretted like a bairn —
But burned the workin'-plans last run, wi' all I hoped to earn.
Ye know how hard an Idol dies, an' what that meant to
    me —
E'en tak' it for a sacrifice acceptable to Thee. . . .
Below there !   Oiler !   What's your wark ?   Ye find it runnin'
    hard ?
Ye needn't swill the cup wi' oil — this isn't the Cunard !
Ye thought ?   Ye are not paid to think.   Go, sweat that off
    again !
Tck !   Tck !   It's deeficult to sweer nor tak' The Name in
    vain !
Men, ay an' women, call me stern.   Wi' these to oversee,
Ye'll note I've little time to burn on social repartee.
The bairns see what their elders miss ; they'll hunt me to an'
    fro,
Till for the sake of — well, a kiss — I tak' 'em down below.

That minds me of our Viscount loon — Sir Kenneth's kin —
   the chap
Wi' Russia leather tennis-shoon an' spar-decked yachtin'-
   cap.
I showed him round last week, o'er all — an' at the last says
   he :
'Mister McAndrew, don't you think steam spoils romance
   at sea ?'
Damned ijjit ! I'd been doon that morn to see what ailed
   the throws,
Manholin', on my back — the cranks three inches off my
   nose.
Romance ! Those first-class passengers they like it very
   well,
Printed an' bound in little books ; but why don't poets
   tell ?
I'm sick of all their quirks an' turns — the loves an' doves
   they dream —
Lord, send a man like Robbie Burns to sing the Song o'
   Steam !
To match wi' Scotia's noblest speech yon orchestra sublime
Whaurto — uplifted like the Just — the tail-rods mark the
   time.
The crank-throws give the double-bass, the feed-pump sobs
   an' heaves,
An' now the main eccentrics start their quarrel on the
   sheaves :
Her time, her own appointed time, the rocking link-head
   bides,
Till — hear that note ? — the rod's return whings glimmerin'
   through the guides.
They're all awa' ! True beat, full power, the clangin' chorus
   goes
Clear to the tunnel where they sit, my purrin' dynamos.
Interdependence, absolute, foreseen, ordained, decreed,
To work, Ye'll note, at ony tilt an' every rate o' speed.
Fra' skylight-lift to furnace-bars, backed, bolted, braced an'
   stayed.

An' singin' like the Mornin' Stars for joy that they are made ;
While, out o' touch o' vanity, the sweatin' thrust-block
    says :
'Not unto us the praise, or man — not unto us the praise !'
Now, a' together, hear them lift their lesson — theirs an'
    mine :
'Law, Orrder, Duty an' Restraint, Obedience, Discipline !'
Mill, forge an' try-pit taught them that when roarin' they
    arose,
An' whiles I wonder if a soul was gied them wi' the blows.
Oh for a man to weld it then, in one trip-hammer strain,
Till even first-class passengers could tell the meanin' plain !
But no one cares except mysel' that serve an' understand
My seven thousand horse-power here. Eh, Lord ! They're
    grand — they're grand !
Uplift am I ? When first in store the new-made beasties
    stood,
Were Ye cast down that breathed the Word declarin' all
    things good ?
Not so ! O' that warld-liftin' joy no after-fall could vex,
Ye've left a glimmer still to cheer the Man — the Arrtifex !
That holds, in spite o' knock and scale, o' friction, waste an'
    slip,
An' by that light — now, mark my word — we'll build the
    Perfect Ship.
I'll never last to judge her lines or take her curve — not I.
But I ha' lived an' I ha' worked. Be thanks to Thee, Most
    High !
An' I ha' done what I ha' done — judge Thou if ill or well —
Always Thy Grace preventin' me. . . .

                       Losh ! Yon's the 'Stand-by' bell.
Pilot so soon ? His flare it is. The mornin'-watch is set.
Well, God be thanked, as I was sayin', I'm no Pelagian yet.
Now I'll tak' on. . . .

  '*Morrn, Ferguson. Man, have ye ever thought*
What your good leddy costs in coal ? . . . I'll burn 'em down to
    port.

RUDYARD KIPLING, The Seven Seas (1896)

Rudyard Kipling

THE SECRET OF THE MACHINES

WE were taken from the ore-bed and the mine,
   We were melted in the furnace and the pit —
We were cast and wrought and hammered to design,
   We were cut and filed and tooled and gauged to fit.
Some water, coal, and oil is all we ask,
   And a thousandth of an inch to give us play :
And now, if you will set us to our task,
   We will serve you four and twenty hours a day !

     We can pull and haul and push and lift and drive,
     We can print and plough and weave and heat and light,
     We can run and jump and swim and fly and dive,
     We can see and hear and count and read and write !

Would you call a friend from half across the world ?
   If you'll let us have his name and town and state,
You shall see and hear your crackling question hurled
   Across the arch of heaven while you wait.
Has he answered ? Does he need you at his side ?
   You can start this very evening if you choose,
And take the Western Ocean in the stride
   Of seventy thousand horses and some screws !

     The boat-express is waiting your command !
     You will find the *Mauretania* at the quay,
     Till her captain turns the lever 'neath his hand,
     And the monstrous nine-decked city goes to sea.

Do you wish to make the mountains bare their head
   And lay their new-cut forests at your feet ?
Do you want to turn a river in its bed,
   Or plant a barren wilderness with wheat ?
Shall we pipe aloft and bring you water down
   From the never-failing cisterns of the snows,
To work the mills and tramways in your town,
   And irrigate your orchards as it flows ?

It is easy ! Give us dynamite and drills !
Watch the iron-shouldered rocks lie down and quake,
As the thirsty desert-level floods and fills,
And the valley we have dammed becomes a lake.

But remember, please, the Law by which we live,
   We are not built to comprehend a lie,
We can neither love nor pity nor forgive.
   If you make a slip in handling us you die !
We are greater than the Peoples or the Kings —
   Be humble, as you crawl beneath our rods ! —
Our touch can alter all created things,
   We are everything on earth — except The Gods !

Though our smoke may hide the Heavens from your eyes,
It will vanish and the stars will shine again,
Because, for all our power and weight and size,
We are nothing more than children of your brain !

RUDYARD KIPLING, A School History of England (1911)

HYMN OF BREAKING STRAIN

THE careful text-books measure
   (Let all who build beware !)
The load, the shock, the pressure
   Material can bear.
So, when the faulty girder
   Lets down the grinding span,
The blame of loss, or murder,
   Is laid upon the man.
       Not on the Stuff — the Man !

But, in our daily dealing
   With stone and steel, we find
The Gods have no such feeling
   Of justice toward mankind.

To no set gauge they make us, —
    For no laid course prepare —
And presently o'ertake us
    With loads we cannot bear :
        Too merciless to bear !

The prudent text-books give it
    In tables at the end —
The stress that shears a rivet
    Or makes a tie-bar bend —
What traffic wrecks macadam —
    What concrete should endure —
But we, poor Sons of Adam,
    Have no such literature,
        To warn us or make sure !

We hold all earth to plunder —
    All Time and Space as well —
Too wonder-stale to wonder
    At each new miracle ;
Till, in the mid-illusion
    Of Godhead 'neath our hand,
Falls multiplied confusion
    On all we did and planned —
        The mighty works we planned.

We only, of Creation
    (Ah luckier bridge and rail !)
Abide the twin-damnation —
    To fail and know we fail.
Yet we — by which sole token
    We know we once were Gods —
Take shame in being broken
    However great the odds —
        The burden or the odds.

Oh veiled and secret Power
    Whose paths we search in vain,

Be with us in our hour
  Of overthrow and pain ;
That we — by which sure token
  We know Thy ways are true —
In spite of being broken —
  Because of being broken —
    May rise and build anew.
    Stand up and build anew !

RUDYARD KIPLING, in Supplement to
The Engineer (15th March 1935)

THE SUBMARINE

SHE slideth through the green sea-night,
Certain and cruel without light ;
In ocean glooms her deaths are done,
She craves no comfort of the Sun.

She striketh low, she striketh sure,
No armour shall her thrust endure ;
The Iron-clad quails through every tower,
Subsiding in elaborate power.

No mailed fortress then shall save
That metal mountain of the wave,
No mounded castle of the deck,
No yawning guns that yearn to speak.

Once in the clear and cruder days
A man might see the lunge that slays ;
The point he strove to baffle well,
Missed, but not all in blindness fell.

But no man knoweth where She steals,
If far away or at our keels ;

Stephen Phillips

Sudden She strikes without a sound,
And leaves a mute but mortal wound.

What clamour of old ocean-war,
What thunder belched at Trafalgar,
Matches in terror the unseen
Stab of the silent Submarine ?

So, late in time has come to be
This man-built menace of the sea ;
God gave no monster to the main
To make the works of man so vain.

STEPHEN PHILLIPS, Lyrics and Dramas (1913)

NEWDIGATE POEM

*A Prize Poem submitted by Mr. Lambkin of Burford to the Examiners
of the University of Oxford on the prescribed poetic theme set by them
in 1893, 'The Benefits of the Electric Light'*

HAIL, Happy Muse, and touch the tuneful string !
The benefits conferred by Science I sing.
  Under the kind Examiners' direction
I only write about them in connection
With benefits which the Electric Light
Confers on us ; especially at night.
These are my theme, of these my song shall rise.
My lofty head shall swell to strike the skies.
And tears of hopeless love bedew the maiden's eyes.
  Descend, O Muse, from thy divine abode,
  To Osney, on the Seven Bridges Road ;
For under Osney's solitary shade
The bulk of the Electric Light is made.
Here are the works ; — from hence the current flows
Which (so the Company's prospectus goes)

Can furnish to Subscribers hour by hour
No less than sixteen thousand candle power,
All at a thousand volts. (It is essential
To keep the current at this high potential
In spite of the considerable expense.)
The Energy developed represents,
Expressed in foot-tons, the united forces
Of fifteen elephants and forty horses.
But shall my scientific detail thus
Clip the dear wings of Buoyant Pegasus ?
Shall pure statistics jar upon the ear
That pants for Lyric accents loud and clear ?
Shall I describe the complex Dynamo
Or write about its Commutator ? No !
To happier fields I lead my wanton pen,
The proper study of mankind is men.
Awake, my Muse ! Portray the pleasing sight
That meets us where they make Electric Light.
Behold the Electrician where he stands :
Soot, oil, and verdigris are on his hands ;
Large spots of grease defile his dirty clothes,
The while his conversation drips with oaths.
Shall such a being perish in its youth ?
Alas ! It is indeed the fatal truth.
In that dull brain, beneath that hair unkempt,
Familiarity has bred contempt.
We warn him of the gesture all too late :
Oh, Heartless Jove ! Oh, Adamantine Fate !
Some random touch — a hand's imprudent slip —
The Terminals — a flash — a sound like 'Zip !'
A smell of burning fills the started Air —
The Electrician is no longer there !
But let us turn with true Artistic scorn
From facts funereal and from views forlorn
Of Erebus and Blackest midnight born.
Arouse thee, Muse ! and chaunt in accents rich
The interesting processes by which
The Electricity is passed along :

These are my theme : to these I bend my song.
It runs encased in wood or porous brick
Through copper wires two millimetres thick,
And insulated on their dangerous mission
By indiarubber, silk, or composition.
Here you may put with critical felicity
The following question : 'What is Electricity ?'
'Molecular Activity,' say some,
Others when asked say nothing, and are dumb.
Whatever be its nature, this is clear :
The rapid current checked in its career,
Baulked in its race and halted in its course
Transforms to heat and light its latent force :
It needs no pedant in the lecturer's chair
To prove that light and heat are present there.
The pear-shaped vacuum globe, I understand,
Is far too hot to fondle with the hand.
While, as is patent to the meanest sight,
The carbon filament is very bright.

As for the lights they hang about the town,
Some praise them highly, others run them down.
This system (technically called the Arc),
Makes some passages too light, others too dark.

But in the house the soft and constant rays
Have always met with universal praise.

For instance : if you want to read in bed
No candle burns beside your curtain's head,
Far from some distant corner of the room
The incandescent lamp dispels the gloom,
And with the largest print need hardly try
The powers of any young and vigorous eye.

Aroint thee, Muse ! Inspired the poet sings !
I cannot help observing future things !
Life is a vale, its paths are dark and rough
Only because we do not know enough :
When Science has discovered something more
We shall be happier than we were before.

Hail, Britain, Mistress of the Azure Main,

Ten thousand Fleets sweep over thee in vain !
Hail, Mighty Mother of the Brave and Free,
That beat Napoleon, and gave birth to me !
Thou that canst wrap in thine emblazoned robe
One quarter of the habitable globe.
Thy mountains, wafted by a favouring breeze,
Like mighty rocks withstand the stormy seas.
   Thou art a Christian Commonwealth ; and yet
Be thou not all unthankful — nor forget
As thou exultest in Imperial Might
The Benefits of the Electric Light.

HILAIRE BELLOC, Verses (1910)

THE DUNCE

AND 'Science' said,
'Attention, Child, to me !
Have I not taught you all
You touch ; taste ; hear ; and see ?

'Nought that's true knowledge now
In print is pent
Which my sole method
Did not circumvent.

'Think you, the amoeba
In its primal slime
Wasted on dreams
Its destiny sublime ?

'Yet, when I bid
Your eyes survey the board
Whereon life's How, When, Where
I now record,

'I find them fixed
In daydream ; and you sigh ;
Or, like a silly sheep,
You bleat me, *Why* ?

'"Why is the grass so cool, and fresh, and green ?
The sky so deep, and blue ?"
Get to your Chemistry,
You dullard, you !

'"Why must I sit at books, and learn, and learn,
Yet long to play ?"
Where's your Psychology,
You popinjay ?

'"Why stay I here,
Not where my heart would be ?"
Wait, dunce, and ask that
Of Philosophy !

'Reason is yours
Wherewith to con your task ;
Not that unanswerable
Questions you should ask.

'Stretch out your hands, then —
Grubby, shallow bowl —
And be refreshed, Child —
Mind, and, maybe, soul !

'Then — when you grow into
A man — like me ;
You will as learnèd, wise,
And — happy be !'

WALTER DE LA MARE, *Inward Companion* (1950)

TO IRON-FOUNDERS AND OTHERS

WHEN you destroy a blade of grass
  You poison England at her roots :
Remember no man's foot can pass
  Where evermore no green life shoots.

You force the birds to wing too high
  Where your unnatural vapours creep :
Surely the living rocks shall die
  When birds no rightful distance keep.

You have brought down the firmament,
  And yet no heaven is more near ;
You shape huge deeds without event,
  And half-made men believe and fear.

Your worship is your furnaces,
  Which, like old idols, lost obscenes,
Have molten bowels ; your vision is
  Machines for making more machines.

O, you are busied in the night,
  Preparing destinies of rust ;
Iron misused must turn to blight
  And dwindle to a tettered crust.

The grass, forerunner of life, has gone ;
  But plants that spring in ruins and shards
Attend until your dream is done :
  I have seen hemlock in your yards.

The generations of the worm
  Know not your loads piled on their soil ;
Their knotted ganglions shall wax firm
  Till your strong flagstones heave and toil.

When the old hollowed earth is cracked,
   And when, to grasp more power and feasts,
Its ores are emptied, wasted, lacked,
   The middens of your burning beasts

Shall be raked over till they yield
   Last priceless slags for fashionings high,
Ploughs to wake grass in every field,
   Chisels men's hands to magnify.

                   (1908)

        GORDON BOTTOMLEY, *Poems of Thirty Years* (1925)

NEW FARM TRACTOR

SNUB nose, the guts of twenty mules are in your cylinders
   and transmission.
The rear axles hold the kick of twenty Missouri jackasses.
It is in the records of the patent office and the ads there is
   twenty horsepower pull here.
The farm boys says hello to you instead of twenty mules —
   he sings to you instead of ten span of mules.
A bucket of oil and a can of grease is your hay and oats.
Rain proof and fool proof they stable you anywhere in the
   fields with the stars for a roof.
I carve a team of long ear mules on the steering wheel — it's
   good-by now to leather reins and the songs of the old
   mule skinners.

        CARL SANDBURG, *Smoke and Steel* (1920)

MR. ATTILA

   THEY made a myth of you, professor,
      you of the gentle voice,
      the books, the specs,
      the furtive rabbit manners

in the mortar-board cap
and the medieval gown.

They didn't think it, eh professor ?
On account of you're so absent-minded,
you bumping into the tree and saying,
'Excuse me, I thought you were a tree,'
passing on again blank and absent-minded.

Now it's 'Mr. Attila, *how* do you do ?'
Do you pack wallops of wholesale death ?
Are you the practical dynamic son-of-a-gun ?
Have you come through with a few abstractions ?
Is it you Mr. Attila we hear saying,
'I beg your pardon but we believe we have made
    some degree of progress on the residual
    qualities of the atom' ?

(August, 1945)

CARL SANDBURG, Complete Poems (1950)

THE OBSERVATORY

AT noon, upon the mountain's purple height,
Above the pine-woods and the clouds it shone
No larger than the small white dome of shell
Left by the fledgling wren when wings are born.
By night it joined the company of heaven,
And, with its constant light, became a star.
A needle-point of light, minute, remote,
It sent a subtler message through the abyss,
Held more significance for the seeing eye
Than all the darkness that would blot it out,
Yet could not dwarf it.

High in heaven it shone,

Alive with all the thoughts, and hopes, and dreams
Of man's adventurous mind.
                  Up there, I knew
The explorers of the sky, a quiet throng
Of pioneers, made ready to attack
That darkness once again, and win new worlds.
To-morrow night they hoped to crown the toil
Of twenty years, and turn upon the sky
The noblest weapon ever made by man.
War had delayed them. They had been drawn away
Designing darker weapons. But no gun
Could outrange this.

'To-morrow night' — so wrote their chief — 'we try
Our great new telescope, the hundred-inch.
Your Milton's "optic tube" has grown in power
Since Galileo, famous, blind, and old,
Talked with him, in that prison, of the sky.
We creep to power by inches. Europe trusts
Her "giant forty" still. Even to-night
Our own old sixty has its work to do ;
And now our hundred-inch . . . I hardly dare
To think what this new muzzle of ours may find.
Come up, and spend that night among the stars
Here, on our mountain-top. If all goes well,
Then, at the least, my friend, you'll see a moon
Stranger, but nearer, many a thousand mile
Than earth has ever seen her, even in dreams.
As for the stars, if seeing them were all,
Three thousand million new-found points of light
Is our rough guess. But never speak of this.
You know our press. They'd miss the one result
To flash "three thousand millions" round the world.'
To-morrow night ! For more than twenty years
They had thought and planned and worked.
   Ten years had gone,
One-fourth, or more, of man's brief working-life,
Before they made those solid tons of glass,

Their hundred-inch reflector, the clear pool,
The polished flawless pool that it must be
To hold the perfect image of a star.
And, even now, some secret flaw — none knew
Until to-morrow's test — might waste it all.
Where was the gambler that would stake so much, —
Time, patience, treasure, on a single throw?
The cost of it, — they'd not find that again,
Either in gold or life-stuff! All their youth
Was fuel to the flame of this one work.
Once in a lifetime to the man of science,
Despite what fools believe his ice-cooled blood,
There comes this drama.
                             If he fails, he fails
Utterly. He at least will have no time
For fresh beginnings. Other men, no doubt,
Years hence, will use the footholes that he cut
In those precipitous cliffs, and reach the height,
But he will never see it.
                             So for me,
The light words of that letter seemed to hide
The passion of a lifetime, and I shared
The crowning moment of its hope and fear.

Next day, through whispering aisles of palm we rode
Up to the foot-hills, dreaming desert-hills
That to assuage their own delicious drought
Had set each tawny sun-kissed slope ablaze
With peach and orange orchards.
                             Up and up,
Along the thin white trail that wound and climbed
And zig-zagged through the grey-green mountain
     sage,
The car went crawling, till the shining plain
Below it, like an airman's map, unrolled.
Houses and orchards dwindled to white specks
In midget cubes and squares of tufted green.
Once, as we rounded one steep curve, that made

The head swim at the canyoned gulf below,
We saw through thirty miles of lucid air
Elvishly small, sharp as a crumpled petal
Blown from the stem, a yard away, a sail
Lazily drifting on the warm blue sea.
Up for nine miles along that spiral trail
Slowly we wound to reach the lucid height
Above the clouds, where that white dome of shell,
No wren's now, but an eagle's, took the flush
Of dying day. The sage-brush all died out,
And all the southern growths, and round us now,
Firs of the north, and strong, storm-rooted pines
Exhaled a keener fragrance ; till, at last,
Reversing all the laws of lesser hills,
They towered like giants round us. Darkness fell
Before we reached the mountain's naked height.

Over us, like some great cathedral dome,
The observatory loomed against the sky ;
And the dark mountain with its headlong gulfs
Had lost all memory of the world below ;
For all those cloudless throngs of glittering stars,
And all those glimmerings where the abyss of space
Is powdered with a milky dust, each grain
A burning sun, and every sun the lord
Of its own darkling planets, — all those lights
Met, in a darker deep, the lights of earth,
Lights on the sea, lights of invisible towns,
Trembling and indistinguishable from stars,
In those black gulfs around the mountain's feet.
Then, into the glimmering dome, with bated breath,
We entered, and, above us, in the gloom
Saw that majestic weapon of the light
Uptowering like the shaft of some huge gun
Through one arched rift of sky.
                              Dark at its base
With naked arms, the crew that all day long
Had sweated to make ready for this night

Waited their captain's word.

                    The switchboard shone
With elfin lamps of white and red, and keys
Whence, at a finger's touch, that monstrous tube
Moved like a creature dowered with life and will,
To peer from deep to deep.

                 Below it pulsed
The clock-machine that slowly, throb by throb,
Timed to the pace of the revolving earth,
Drove the titanic muzzle on and on,
Fixed to the chosen star that else would glide
Out of its field of vision.

             So, set free
Balanced against the wheel of time, it swung,
Or rested, while, to find new realms of sky
The dome that housed it, like a moon revolved,
So smoothly that the watchers hardly knew
They moved within ; till, through the glimmering doors,
They saw the dark procession of the pines
Like Indian warriors, quietly stealing by.

Then, at a word, the mighty weapon dipped
Its muzzle and aimed at one small point of light,
One seeming insignificant star.

               The chief,
Mounting the ladder, while we held our breath,
Looked through the eye-piece.

           Then we heard him laugh
His thanks to God, and hide it in a jest.
'A prominence on Jupiter !' —

                They laughed,
'What do you mean ?' — 'It's moving,' cried the chief,
They laughed again, and watched his glimmering face
High overhead against that moving tower.
'Come up and see, then !'

            One by one they went,
And, though each laughed as he returned to earth,
Their souls were in their eyes.

                                    Then I, too, looked,
And saw that insignificant spark of light
Touched with new meaning, beautifully reborn,
A swimming world, a perfect rounded pearl,
Poised in the violet sky ; and, as I gazed,
I saw a miracle, — right on its upmost edge
A tiny mound of white that slowly rose,
Then, like an exquisite seed-pearl, swung quite clear
And swam in heaven above its parent world
To greet its three bright sister-moons.
                                    A moon,
Of Jupiter, no more, but clearer far
Than mortal eyes had seen before from earth.
Beautiful, keen and clear beyond all dreams
Was that one silver phrase of the starry tune
Which Galileo's 'old discoverer' first
Dimly revealed, dissolving into clouds
The imagined fabric of our universe.
'*Jupiter stands in heaven and will stand*
Though all the sycophants bark at him,' he cried,
Hailing the truth before he, too, went down,
Whelmed in the cloudy wreckage of that dream.

So one by one we looked, the men who served
Urania, and the men from Vulcan's forge.
A beautiful eagerness in the darkness lit
The swarthy faces that too long had missed
A meaning in the dull mechanic maze
Of labour on this blind earth, but found it now.
Though only a moment's wandering melody
Hopelessly far above, it gave their toil
Its only consecration and its joy.
There, with dark-smouldering eyes and naked throats,
Blue-dungareed, red-shirted, grimed and smeared
With engine-grease and sweat, they gathered round
The foot of that dim ladder ; each muttering low
As he came down, his wonder at what he saw
To those who waited, — a picture for the brush

Of Rembrandt, lighted only by the rift
Above them, where the giant muzzle thrust
Out through the dim arched roof, and slowly throbbed,
Against the slowly moving wheel of the earth,
Holding their chosen star.

> There, like an elf,
Perched on the side of that dark slanting tower,
The Italian mechanician watched the moons
That Italy discovered.

> One by one,
English, American, French, and Dutch, they climbed
To see the wonder that their own blind hands
Had helped to achieve.

> At midnight while they paused
To adjust the clock-machine, I wandered out
Alone, into the silence of the night.
The silence ? On that lonely height I heard
Eternal voices ;
For, as I looked into the gulf beneath,
Whence almost all the lights had vanished now,
The whole dark mountain seemed to have lost its earth
And to be sailing like a ship through heaven.
All round it surged the mighty sea-like sound
Of soughing pine-woods, one vast ebb and flow
Of absolute peace, aloof from all earth's pain,
So calm, so quiet, it seemed the cradle-song,
The deep soft breathing of the universe
Over its youngest child, the soul of man.
And, as I listened, that Æolian voice
Became an invocation and a prayer :
O you, that on your loftier mountain dwell
And move like light in light among the thoughts
Of heaven, translating our mortality
Into immortal song, is there not one
Among you that can turn to music now
This long dark fight for truth ? Not one to touch
With beauty this long battle for the light,
This little victory of the spirit of man

Doomed to defeat — for what was all we saw
To that which neither eyes nor soul could see ? —
Doomed to defeat and yet unconquerable,
Climbing its nine miles nearer to the stars.
Wars we have sung. The blind, blood-boltered kings
Move with an epic music to their thrones.
Have you no song, then, of that nobler war ?
Of those who strove for light, but could not dream
Even of this victory that they helped to win,
Silent discoverers, lonely pioneers,
Prisoners and exiles, martyrs of the truth
Who handed on the fire, from age to age ;
Of those who, step by step, drove back the night
And struggled, year on year, for one more glimpse
Among the stars, of sovran law, their guide ;
Of those who searching inward, saw the rocks
Dissolving into a new abyss, and saw
Those planetary systems far within,
Atoms, electrons, whirling on their way
To build and to unbuild our solid world ;
Of those who conquered, inch by difficult inch,
The freedom of this realm of law for man ;
Dreamers of dreams, the builders of our hope,
The healers and the binders up of wounds,
Who, while the dynasts drenched the world with blood,
Would in the still small circle of a lamp
Wrestle with death like Heracles of old
To save one stricken child.
                              Is there no song
To touch this moving universe of law
With ultimate light, the glimmer of that great dawn
Which over our ruined altars yet shall break
In purer splendour, and restore mankind
From darker dreams that even Lucretius knew,
To vision of that one Power which guides the world.
How should men find it ? Only through those doors
Which, opening inward, in each separate soul
Give each man access to that Soul of all

Living within each life, not to be found
Or known, till, looking inward, each alone
Meets the unknowable and eternal God.

And there was one that moved like light in light
Before me there, — Love, human and divine,
That can exalt all weakness into power, —
Whispering, *Take this deathless torch of song* . . .
Whispering, but with such faith, that even I
Was humbled into thinking this might be
Through love, though all the wisdom of the world
Account it folly.   Let my breast be bared
To every shaft, then, so that Love be still
My one celestial guide the while I sing
Of those who caught the pure Promethean fire
One from another, each crying as he went down
To one that waited, crowned with youth and joy, —
Take thou the splendour, carry it out of sight
Into the great new age I must not know,
Into the great new realm I must not tread.

> From ALFRED NOYES, *The Torch-Bearers*, Vol. 1 (1922)

THE STEAM-GIVERS

(*Parody* — *Alfred Noyes*)

PART I

AUSTERE, remote, immeasurably proud
And filled with shining levers that control
The health and happiness of half the world
The signal cabin at East Croydon Main
Beckoned me upwards.

                    For the signalman
Had said, 'To-morrow, if you care to see

E. V. Knox

The way the London, Brighton and South Coast
Directs her passing traffic, you may come';
And I said, 'Right-o.'

                 When I went upstairs
I found a calmness. More significant
That calm than all the busy toil below;
That calm than all the shrieking of the trains
That strove to rend it. Dominant, serene,
That signal box with all its telephones,
The train and sinews of a host of arms,
Prophetically reared or dropped to rest,
The sun and centre of a host of stars
That shimmer through the darkness of our night:
Sole guide to all those intermingling threads
Of silvern rivers running to the sea,
Of main and branch lines bounded by the sea,
Fraught with innumerable ballast trains,
And steering onward to predestined ends
Express and ordinary passengers —
There in that box I found a windless calm.
I saw the needles pointing to 'Line clear,'
'Train out of section,' or to 'Train on line';
I heard the bells beat, many different bells
Beating with different tones for 'up' and 'down',
With different pauses in between the bells
For different trains, carrying cattle and men,
Fruit, meat and milk and perishable goods,
Breakdowns and empties.

                 I observed the clocks
And all the various gadgets everywhere
Connected with the interlocking frame,
The levers, red and white and black and green,
And tried to understand the lock and block
System itself; but I was foiled by that.
Aye! lock and block, ye were too much for me!
But as I tried I seemed to hear a voice,

A voice between the tinklings of the bells,
That said, 'We were the fathers'; seemed to see
Shadows of those great spirits of the past,
Silent discoverers, lonely pioneers;
And first of all that one who, handing on
The spark of fire from the immense profound,
Improved the stationary steam engine
And made it fit for locomotive use.

He was a great mechanic, was James Watt,
Of lowland stock, too weakly as a child
For regular attendances at school,
So that quite often, when the school-bell splashed
The air with sound, he stayed beside the fire.
Much from his mother's teaching he would learn,
Much from his father's; but still more he taught
Himself unaided.

            At nineteen his love
For making mathematic instruments
Lured him to London. But, returning thence
To Glasgow, Glasgow proved unkind to him,
His more than common capabilities
Provoking strange hostility among
The Incorporated Guild of Hammermen;
Till wiser souls than theirs, more apt to see
How light leaps forth from learning, knowledge springs
Ever from seeking knowledge, not routine,
Helped the ingenious James and found him an
Appointment at the University.

He was a great mechanic, was James Watt.
And whether now, as some would have it first,
Or earlier in the cottage where he toiled
Beside the firelight, and one day at tea,
Seeing the kettle's lifted lid (such power
The boiling water had to heave the thing
Upward), he turned his adolescent mind

E. V. Knox

To muse upon the motive strength of steam —
Thus much is sure, that, always murmuring 'Steam',
And 'Steam, more steam', he hit as in a flash
One day on that sublime experiment,
The separate condenser, which o'ercame
The loss of steam inside the cylinder.

He was a great mechanic, was James Watt.
And ever as he toiled and murmured 'Steam'
He sang some stave to wile the weary hours
And break the page, some little stave like this —

In Old Cathay, in far Cathay
   Before the West espied the gleam,
Philosophers had found no way
   Of fruitfully condensing steam.
With instruments that went by hand
   Their unenlightened path they trod ;
The Chinese did not understand
   The uses of the piston-rod.

On camel-back from Araby
   Transporting frankincense and myrrh,
The old Arabians failed to see
   Much object in a cylinder ;
But where is Araby by now ?
   She fades away and is forgot,
While all the world remembers how
   The steam-engine was built by Watt.

The lion wanders round at nights
   Where Jamshid made a marble tower
According to his simple lights
   With merely manual motive power ;
Dishonoured now is Jamshid laid
   In desert courts where once he drank ;
He might have done far more for trade
   By using my ingenious crank.

In Babylon, in Babylon,
   They frittered half their time away
With futile variations on
   Contrivances that did not pay ;
For Belus' sake they built a shrine,
   But Belus now is dead and gone ;
And fly-wheels much resembling mine
   Will soon be used in Babylon.

So singing always as he laboured on,
Watt worked at engines, till at last his life
Drew to a tranquil and an honoured close
At Heathfield, fairly near to Birmingham.
And though they say he never would consent
To smile upon the tractive use of steam,
And even put a clause into his lease
That no steam carriage should approach his house,
Yet paved the path for Stephenson to build
The earliest locomotive.

        So he died.
He was a great mechanic, was James Watt.
        E. V. KNOX, *These Liberties* (1923)

OVERTURE TO A DANCE OF LOCOMOTIVES

MEN with picked voices chant the names
of cities in a huge gallery : promises
that pull through descending stairways
to a deep rumbling.

      The rubbing feet
to those coming to be carried quicken a
grey pavement into soft light that rocks

to and fro, under the domed ceiling,
across and across from pale
earthcolored walls of bare limestone.

Covertly the hands of a great clock
go round and round ! Were they to
move quickly and at once the whole
secret would be out and the shuffling
of all ants be done forever.

A leaning pyramid of sunlight, narrowing
out at a high window, moves by the clock ;
discordant hands straining out from
a center : inevitable postures infinitely
repeated —

two — twofour — twoeight !

Porters in red hats run on narrow platforms.

This way ma'am !
                              — important not to take
the wrong train !
                              Lights from the concrete
ceiling hang crooked but —
                              Poised horizontal
on glittering parallels the dingy cylinders
packed with a warm glow — inviting entry —
pull against the hour. But brakes can
hold a fixed posture till —
                              The whistle !

Not twoeight. Not twofour. Two !

Gliding windows. Colored cooks sweating
in a small kitchen. Taillights —
In time : twofour !
In time : twoeight !

— rivers are tunneled : trestles
cross oozy swampland : wheels repeating
the same gesture remain relatively
stationary : rails forever parallel
return on themselves infinitely.
                              The dance is sure.

                    WILLIAM CARLOS WILLIAMS, written *c.* 1913

IN CONTINUATION OF POPE
ON NEWTON

NATURE and Nature's laws lay hid in night :
God said, 'Let Newton be !' and all was light.

IT did not last : the Devil howling 'Ho,
Let Einstein be,' restored the status quo.

                    SIR JOHN SQUIRE, *Poems in
                    One Volume* (1926)

THE TRIUMPH OF THE MACHINE

THEY talk of the triumph of the machine,
but the machine will never triumph.

Out of the thousands and thousands of centuries of man
the unrolling of ferns, white tongues of the acanthus lapping
        at the sun,
for one sad century
machines have triumphed, rolled us hither and thither,
shaking the lark's nest till the eggs have broken.

Shaken the marshes till the geese have gone
and the wild swans flown away singing the swan-song of us.

D. H. Lawrence

Hard, hard on the earth the machines are rolling,
but through some hearts they will never roll.

The lark nests in his heart
and the white swan swims in the marshes of his loins,
and through the wide prairies of his breast a young bull herds
    the cows,
lambs frisk among the daisies of his brain.

And at last
all these creatures that cannot die, driven back
into the innermost corners of the soul
will send up the wild cry of despair.

The trilling lark in a wild despair will trill down from the
    sky,
The swan will beat the waters in rage, white rage of an
    enraged swan,
even the lambs will stretch forth their necks like serpents,
like snakes of hate, against the man in the machine :
even the shaking white poplar will dazzle like splinters of
    glass against him.

And against this inward revolt of the native creatures of the
    soul
mechanical man, in triumph seated upon the seat of his
    machine
will be powerless, for no engine can reach into the marshes
    and depths of a man.

So mechanical man in triumph seated upon the seat of his
    machine
will be driven mad from himself, and sightless, and on that
    day
the machines will turn to run into one another
traffic will tangle up in a long-drawn-out crash of collision
and engines will rush at the solid houses, the edifice of our
    life

P
209

will rock in the shock of the mad machine, and the house
will come down.

Then, far beyond the ruin, in the far, in the ultimate, remote
places
the swan will lift up again his flattened, smitten head,
and look round, and rise, and on the great vaults of his
wings
will sweep round and up to greet the sun with a silky glitter
of a new day
and the lark will follow trilling, angerless again,
and the lambs will bite off the heads of the daisies for friski-
ness.
But over the middle of the earth will be the smoky ruin of
iron
the triumph of the machine.

D. H. LAWRENCE, Last Poems (1932)

FIFTH PHILOSOPHER'S SONG

A MILLION million spermatozoa,
   All of them alive :
Out of their cataclysm but one poor Noah
   Dare hope to survive.

And among that billion minus one
   Might have chanced to be
Shakespeare, another Newton, a new Donne —
   But the One was Me.

Shame to have ousted your betters thus,
   Taking ark while the others remained outside !
Better for all of us, froward Homunculus,
   If you'd quietly died !

ALDOUS HUXLEY, Leda (1920)

210

Edmund Blunden

THE SCIENTISTS

How shall this thing be done ?
How shall we make the lawless lightning run
In tracks compelled by us, its flame
Obedient grown to us and tame
As water played from marble Triton's gorge ?
What change should seize this passionate fire
And keep him here at our desire,
The courier of our will, the servant of our forge ?

Curious and maybe more
If we might gaze with an intenser eye
Into this star which burns and seems to try
To give us its strange lore.
There is the challenge, here are we aware
Of something in the air ;
And only one thing needed, but that one
May seem faint dream. How shall this thing be done ?

'I'll put a girdle round about the world
In forty seconds.' If you mean a chain
Of thought and news and sense, do not refrain ;
But fancy oiled and curled
Has entertained before. In earnest then
You mean to traverse weather fair or foul,
Speak, sing, play Shakespeare through the hemispheres,
Serene through distance and through tempest's howl —
Bear London's voice to Tokyo ? Gentlemen,
I will subscribe when your machine appears.

Professor, one small doubt
Here is a body, which this morning smiled
A beautiful and energetic child.
What is this wave of life, and whence welled out ?
Why, how so sharply vanished ? Will not you,
Having accomplished such a host of things

Which I repeated *x* times could not do,
Come at this other secret ? Find the nerve,
Discern the essential curve,
And build the new power-station, the reserve ?
You know that easy dust which makes a gun
Immensely active —

           'This too shall be done.'

        EDMUND BLUNDEN, *Poems 1930–1940* (1940)

POWER

THE nasal whine of power whips a new universe . . .
Where spouting pillars spoor the evening sky,
Under the looming stacks of the gigantic power house
Stars prick the eyes with sharp ammoniac proverbs,
New verities, new inklings in the velvet hummed
Of dynamos, where hearing's leash is strummed . . .
Power's script, — wound, bobbin-bound, refined —
Is stropped to the slap of belts on booming spools, spurred
Into the bulging bouillon, harnessed jelly of the stars.
Towards what ? The forked crash of split thunder parts
Our hearing momentwise ; but fast in whirling armatures,
As bright as frogs' eyes, giggling in the girth
Of steely gizzards — axle-bound, confined
In coiled precision, bunched in mutual glee
The bearings glint, — O murmurless and shined
In oilrinsed circles of blind ecstasy !

Stars scribble on our eyes the frosty sagas,
The gleaming cantos of unvanquished space . . .
O sinewy silver biplane, nudging the wind's withers !
There, from Kill Devils Hill at Kitty Hawk
Two brothers in their twinship left the dune ;
Warping the gale, the Wright windwrestlers veered
Capeward, then blading the wind's flank, banked and spun

Hart Crane

What ciphers risen from prophetic script,
What marathons new-set between the stars !
The soul, by naphtha fledged into new reaches,
Already knows the closer clasp of Mars, —
New latitudes, unknotting, soon give place
To what fierce schedules, rife of doom apace !

Behold the dragon's covey — amphibian, ubiquitous
To hedge the seaboard, wrap the headland, ride
The blue's cloud-templed districts unto ether . . .
While Iliads glimmer through eyes raised in pride
Hell's belt springs wider into heaven's plumed side.
O bright circumferences, heights employed to fly
War's fiery kennel masked in downy offings, —
This tournament of space, the threshed and chiselled height,
Is baited by marauding circles, bludgeon flail
Of rancorous grenades whose screaming petals carve us
Wounds that we wrap with theorems sharp as hail !

Wheeled swiftly, wings emerge from larval-silver hangars.
Taut motors surge, space-gnawing, into flight ;
Through sparkling visibility, outspread, unsleeping,
Wings clip the last peripheries of light . . .
Tellurian wind-sleuths on dawn patrol,
Each plane a hurtling javelin of winged ordnance,
Bristle the heights above a screeching gale to hover ;
Surely no eye that Sunward Escadrille can cover !
There, meaningful, fledged as the Pleiades
With razor sheen they zoom each rapid helix !
Up-chartered choristers of their own speeding
They, cavalcade on escapade, shear Cumulus —
Lay siege and hurdle Cirrus down the skies !

From HART CRANE, *The Bridge :*
IV Cape Hatteras (1930)

LA MARCHE DES MACHINES

THIS piston's infinite recurrence is
night morning night and morning night and
death and birth and death and birth and this
crank climbs (blind Sisyphus) and see

steel teeth greet
bow deliberate
delicately lace
in lethal kiss
    God's teeth bite whitely tight

slowly the gigantic oh slowly the steel spine dislocates

wheels grazing (accurately missing) waltz

two cranes do a hundred-ton tango against the sky

   A. S. J. TESSIMOND, in *New Signatures : Poems by*
     several hands, ed. Michael Roberts (1932)

PYLONS

OVER the tree'd upland evenly striding,
One after one they lift their serious shapes
That ring with light.   The statement of their steel
Contradicts nature's softer architecture.
Earth will not accept them as it accepts
A wall, a plough, a church so coloured of earth
It might be some experiment of the soil's.
Yet are they outposts of the trekking future.
Into the thatch-hung consciousness of hamlets
They blaze new thoughts, new habits.
        Traditions
Are being trod down like flowers dropped by children.
Already that farm boy striding and throwing seed

In the shoulder-hinged half-circle Millet knew,
Looks grey with antiquity as his dead forbears,
A half familiar figure out of the Georgics,
Unheeded by these new-world, rational towers.

STANLEY SNAITH, The Silver Scythe (1933)

FLIGHT TO AUSTRALIA

SING we the two lieutenants, Parer and M'Intosh,
After the War wishing to hie them home to Australia,
Planned they would take a high way, a hazardous crazy air-
    way :
Death their foregone conclusion, a flight headlong to failure,
We said. For no silver posh
Plane was their pigeon, no dandy dancer quick-stepping
    through heaven,
But a craft of obsolete design, a condemned D.H. nine ;
Sold for a song it was, patched up though to write an heroic
Line across the world as it reeled on its obstinate stoic
Course to that southern haven.

On January 8, 1920, their curveting wheels kissed
England goodbye. Over Hounslow huddled in morning mist
They rose and circled like buzzards while we rubbed our
    sleepy eyes :
Like a bird scarce-fledged they flew, whose flying hours are
    few —
Still dear is the nest but deeper its desire unto the skies —
And they left us to our sleeping.
They felt earth's warning tug on their wings : vain to
    advance
Asking a thoroughfare through the angers of the air
On so flimsy a frame : but they pulled up her nose and the
    earth went sloping
Away, and they aimed for France.

Fog first, a wet blanket, a kill-joy, the primrose-of-
    morning's blight,
Blotting out the dimpled sea, the ample welcome of land,
The gay glance from the bright
Cliff-face behind, snaring the sky with treachery, sneering
At hope's loss of height.   But they charged it, flying blind ;
They took a compass-bearing against that dealer of doubt,
As a saint when the field of vision is fogged gloriously
    steels
His spirit against the tainter of air, the elusive taunter :
They climbed to win a way out,
Then downward dared till the moody waves snarled at their
    wheels.

Landing at last near Conteville, who had skimmed the crest
    of oblivion,
They could not rest, but rose and flew on to Paris, and there
Trivially were delayed — a defective petrol feed —
Three days : a time hung heavy on
Hand and heart, till they leapt again to the upper air,
Their element, their lover, their angel antagonist.
Would have taken a fall without fame, but the sinewy
    framework the wrist
Of steel the panting engine wrestled well : and they went
South while the going was good, as a swallow that guide nor
    goad
Needs on his sunny scent.

At Lyons the petrol pump failed again, and forty-eight
    hours
They chafed to be off, the haughty champions whose
    breathing-space
Was an horizon span and the four winds their fan.
Over Italy's shores
A reverse, the oil ran out and cursing they turned about
Losing a hundred miles to find a landing-place.
Not a coast for a castaway this, no even chance of alighting
On sward or wind-smooth sand :

A hundred miles without pressure they flew, the engine fighting
For breath, and its heart nearly burst before they dropped to
 land.

And now the earth they had spurned rose up against them in
 anger,
Tier upon tier it towered, the terrible Apennines :
No sanctuary there for wings, not flares nor landing-lines,
No hope of floor and hangar.
Yet those ice-tipped spears that disputed the passage set spurs
To their two hundred and forty horse power ; grimly they
 gained
Altitude, though the hand of heaven was heavy upon them,
The downdraught from the mountains : though desperate
 eddies spun them
Like a coin, yet unkindly tossed their luck came uppermost
And mastery remained.

Air was all ambushes round them, was avalanche earthquake
Quicksand, a funnel deep as doom, till climbing steep
They crawled like a fly up the face of perpendicular night
And levelled, finding a break
At fourteen thousand feet.   Here earth is shorn from sight :
Deadweight a darkness hangs on their eyelids, and they
 bruise
Their eyes against a void : vindictive the cold airs close
Down like a trap of steel and numb them from head to heel ;
Yet they kept an even keel,
For their spirit reached forward and took the controls while
 their fingers froze.

They had not heard the last of death.   When the mountains
 were passed,
He raised another crest, the long crescendo of pain
Kindled to climax, the plane
Took fire.   Alone in the sky with the breath of their enemy
Hot in their face they fought : from three thousand feet
 they tilted

Over, side-slipped away — a trick for an ace, a race
And running duel with death : flame streamed out behind,
A crimson scarf of, as life-blood out of a wound, but the
    wind
Of their downfall staunched it ; death wilted,
Lagged and died out in smoke — he could not stay their
    pace.

A lull for a while. The powers of hell rallied their legions.
On Parer now fell the stress of the flight ; for the plane had
    been bumped,
Buffeted, thrashed by the air almost beyond repair :
But he tinkered and coaxed, and they limped
Over the Adriatic on into warmer regions.
Erratic their course to Athens, to Crete : coolly they rode her
Like a tired horse at the water-jumps, they jockeyed her over
    seas,
Till they came at last to a land whose dynasties of sand
Had seen Alexander, Napoleon, many a straddling invader,
But never none like these.

England to Cairo, a joy-ride, a forty-hour journey at most,
Had cost them forty-four days. What centuried strata of life
Fuelled the fire that haled them to heaven, the power that
    held them
Aloft ? For their plane was a laugh,
A patch, brittle as matchstick, a bubble, a lift for a ghost :
Bolts always working loose of propeller, cylinder, bearer ;
Instruments faulty ; filter, magneto, each strut unsound.
Yet after four days, though we swore she never could leave
    the ground,
We saw her in headstrong haste diminish towards the east —
That makeshift, mad sky-farer.

Aimed they now for Baghdad, unwritten in air's annals
A voyage. But theirs the fate all flights of logic to refute,
Who obeyed no average law, who buoyed the viewless
    channels

Of sky with a courage steadfast, luminous.   Safe they
    crossed
Sinai's desert, and daring
The Nejd, the unneighbourly waste of Arabia, yet higher
    soaring
(Final a fall there for birds of passage, limed and lost
In shifty the sand's embrace) all day they strove to climb
Through stormy rain : but they felt her shorten her stride
    and falter,
And they fell at evening time.

Slept that night beside their machine, and the next morning
Raider Arabs appeared reckoning this stranded bird
A gift : like cobras they struck, and their gliding shadows
    athwart
The sand were all their warning.
But the aeronauts, knowing iron the coinage here, had
    brought
Mills bombs and revolvers, and M'Intosh held them off
While Parer fought for life —
A spark, the mechanic's right answer, and finally wrought
A miracle, for the dumb engine spoke and they rose
Convulsively out of the clutch of the desert, the clench of
    their foes.

Orchestrate this theme, artificer-poet.   Imagine
The roll, crackling percussion, quickening tempo of engine
For a start : the sound as they soar, an octave-upward slur
Scale of sky ascending :
Hours-held note of level flight, a beat unhurried,
Sustaining undertone of movement never-ending :
Wind shrill on the ailerons, flutes and fifes in a flurry
Devilish when they dive, plucking of tense stays.
These hardly heard it, who were the voice, the heavenly air
That sings above always.

We have seen the extremes, the burning, the freezing, the
    outward face

Of their exploit ; heroic peaks, tumbling-to-zero depressions :
Little our graph can show, the line they traced through
    space,
Of the heart's passionate patience.
How soft drifts of sleep piled on their senses deep
And they dug themselves out often : how the plane was a
    weight that hung
And swung on their aching nerve ; how din drilled through
    the skull
And sight sickened — so slow earth filtered past below.
Yet nerve failed never, heart clung
To height, and the brain kept its course and the hand its
    skill.

Baghdad renewed a propeller damaged in desert. Arid
Baluchistan spared them that brought down and spoilt with
    thirst
Armies of Alexander. To Karachi they were carried
On cloud-back : fragile as tinder their plane, but the winds
    were tender
Now to their need, and nursed
Them along till teeming India made room for them to alight
Wilting her wings, the sweltering suns had moulted her
    bright
Plumage, rotten with rain
The fabric : but they packed her with iron washers and
    tacked her
Together, good for an hour, and took the air again.

Feats for a hundred flights, they were prodigal of : a fairest
Now to tell — how they foiled death when the engine failed
Above the Irrawaddy, over close-woven forest.
What shoals for a pilot there, what a snarled passage and
    dark
Shelves down to doom and grip
Of green ! But look, balanced superbly, quick off the mark
Swooping like centre three-quarter whose impetus storms a
    gap —

C. Day Lewis

Defenders routed, rooted their feet, and their arms are mown
Aside, that high or low aim at his overthrow —
M'Intosh touched her down.

And they picked her up out of it somehow and put her at the
    air, a
Sorry hack for such steeplechasing, to leap the sky.
'We'll fly this bloody crate till it falls to bits at our feet,'
Said the mechanic Parer.
And at Moulmein soon they crashed ; and the plane by
    their spirit's high
Tension long pinned, girded and guarded from dissolution,
Fell to bits at their feet. Wrecked was the undercarriage,
Radiator cracked, in pieces, compasses crocked ;
Fallen all to confusion.
Their winged hope was a heap of scrap, but unsplintered
    their courage.

Six weeks they worked in sun-glare and jungle damps,
    assembling
Fragments to make airworthy what was worth not its weight
    in air.
As a surgeon, grafter of skin, as a setter of bones tumbling
Apart, they had power to repair
This good for naught but the grave : they livened her engine
    and gave
Fuselage faith to rise rejuvenated from ruin.
Went with them stowaways, not knowing what hazard they
    flew in —
Bear-cubs, a baby alligator, lizards and snakes galore ;
Mascots maybe, for the plane though twice she was floored
    again
Always came up for more.

Till they came to the pitiless mountains of Timor. Yet these,
    untamed,
Not timorous, against the gradient and Niagara of air they
    climbed

Scarce-skimming the summits ; and over the shark-toothed
    Timor sea
Lost their bearings, but shirked not the odds, the deaths that
    lurked
A million to one on their trail :
They reached out to the horizon and plucked their destiny.
On for eight hours they flew blindfold against the unknown,
And the oil began to fail
And their flying spirit waned — one pint of petrol remained
When the land stood up to meet them and they came into
    their own.

Southward still to Melbourne, the bourn of their flight, they
    pressed
Till at last near Culcairn, like a last fretted leaf
Falling from brave autumn into earth's breast,
D.H. nine, their friend that had seen them to the end,
Gave up her airy life.
The Southern Cross was splendid above the spot where she
    fell,
The end of her rainbow curve over our weeping day :
And the flyers, glad to be home, unharmed by that dizzy fall,
Dazed as the dead awoken from death, stepped out of the
    broken
Body and went away.

C. DAY LEWIS, *A Time to Dance,*
and Other Poems (1935)

THE UNKNOWN CITIZEN

(To JS/07/M/378
This Marble Monument
Is Erected by the State)

HE was found by the Bureau of Statistics to be
One against whom there was no official complaint,

And all the reports on his conduct agree
That, in the modern sense of an old-fashioned word, he was
   a saint,
For in everything he did he served the Greater Community.
Except for the War till the day he retired
He worked in a factory and never got fired,
But satisfied his employers, Fudge Motors Inc.
Yet he wasn't a scab or odd in his views,
For his Union reports that he paid his dues,
(Our report on his Union shows it was sound)
And our Social Psychology workers found
That he was popular with his mates and liked a drink.
The Press are convinced that he bought a paper every day
And that his reactions to advertisements were normal in
   every way.
Policies taken out in his name prove that he was fully
   insured,
And his Health-card shows he was once in hospital but left
   it cured.
Both Producers Research and High-Grade Living declare
He was fully sensible to the advantages of the Instalment
   Plan
And had everything necessary to the Modern Man,
A phonograph, a radio, a car and a frigidaire.
Our researchers into Public Opinion are content
That he held the proper opinions for the time of year ;
When there was peace, he was for peace ; when there was
   war, he went.
He was married and added five children to the population,
Which our Eugenist says was the right number for a parent
   of his generation,
And our teachers report that he never interfered with their
   education.
Was he free ? Was he happy ? The question is absurd :
Had anything been wrong, we should certainly have heard.

W. H. AUDEN, *Another Time* (1940)

IN MEMORY OF SIGMUND FREUD

(d. *September* 1939)

WHEN there are so many we shall have to mourn,
When grief has been made so public, and exposed
  To the critique of a whole epoch
  The frailty of our conscience and anguish,

Of whom shall we speak ? For every day they die
Among us, those who were doing us some good,
  And knew it was never enough but
  Hoped to improve a little by living.

Such was this doctor : still at eighty he wished
To think of our life, from whose unruliness
  So many plausible young futures
  With threats or flattery ask obedience.

But his wish was denied him ; he closed his eyes
Upon that last picture common to us all,
  Of problems like relatives standing
  Puzzled and jealous about our dying.

For about him at the very end were still
Those he had studied, the nervous and the nights,
  And shades that still waited to enter
  The bright circle of his recognition

Turned elsewhere with their disappointment as he
Was taken away from his old interest
  To go back to the earth in London
  An important Jew who died in exile.

Only Hate was happy, hoping to augment
His practice now, and his shabby clientèle
  Who think they can be cured by killing
  And covering the gardens with ashes.

They are still alive but in a world he changed
Simply by looking back with no false regrets ;
  All that he did was to remember
  Like the old and be honest like children.

He wasn't clever at all : he merely told
The unhappy Present to recite the Past
  Like a poetry lesson till sooner
  Or later it faltered at the line where

Long ago the accusations had begun,
And suddenly knew by whom it had been judged,
  How rich life had been and how silly,
  And was life-forgiven and more humble.

Able to approach the Future as a friend
Without a wardrobe of excuses, without
  A set mask of rectitude or an
  Embarrassing over-familiar gesture.

No wonder the ancient cultures of conceit
In his technique of unsettlement foresaw
  The fall of princes, the collapse of
  Their lucrative patterns of frustration.

If he succeeded, why, the Generalized Life
Would become impossible, the monolith
  Of State be broken and prevented
  The co-operation of avengers.

Of course they called on God : but he went his way,
Down among the Lost People like Dante, down
  To the stinking fosse where the injured
  Lead the ugly life of the rejected.

And showed us what evil is : not as we thought
Deeds that must be punished, but our lack of faith,
  Our dishonest mood of denial,
  The concupiscence of the oppressor.

And if something of the autocratic pose,
The paternal strictness he distrusted, still
  Clung to his utterance and features,
  It was a protective imitation.

For one who lived among enemies so long ;
If often he was wrong and at times absurd,
  To us he is no more a person
  Now but a whole climate of opinion,

Under whom we conduct our differing lives :
Like weather he can only hinder or help,
  The proud can still be proud but find it
  A little harder, and the tyrant tries

To make him do but doesn't care for him much.
He quietly surrounds all our habits of growth ;
  He extends, till the tired in even
  The remotest most miserable duchy

Have felt the change in their bones and are cheered,
And the child unlucky in his little State,
  Some hearth where freedom is excluded,
  A hive whose honey is fear and worry,

Feels calmer now and somehow assured of escape ;
While as they lie in the grass of our neglect,
  So many long-forgotten objects
  Revealed by his undiscouraged shining

Are returned to us and made precious again ;
Games we had thought we must drop as we grew up,
  Little noises we dared not laugh at,
  Faces we made when no one was looking.

But he wishes us more than this : to be free
Is often to be lonely ; he would unite
  The unequal moieties fractured
  By our own well-meaning sense of justice.

Would restore to the larger the wit and will
The smaller possesses but can only use
    For arid disputes, would give back to
    The son the mother's richness of feeling.

But he would have us remember most of all
To be enthusiastic over the night
    Not only for the sense of wonder
    It alone has to offer, but also

Because it needs our love : for with sad eyes
Its delectable creatures look up and beg
    Us dumbly to ask them to follow ;
    They are exiles who long for the future

That lies in our power. They too would rejoice
If allowed to serve enlightenment like him,
    Even to bear our cry of ' Judas,'
    As he did and all must bear who serve it.

One rational voice is dumb : over a grave
The household of Impulse mourns one dearly loved.
    Sad is Eros, builder of cities,
    And weeping anarchic Aphrodite.
      W. H. AUDEN, *Collected Shorter Poems 1930–1944* (1950)

ODE TO GAEA

FROM this new culture of the air we finally see,
Far-shining in excellence, what our Mother, the
    Nicest daughter of Chaos, would
  Admire could she look in a glass,

And what, in her eyes, is natural : it is the old
Grand style of gesture we watch as, heavy with cold,

The top-waters of all her
Northern seas take their vernal plunge,

And suddenly her desolations, salt as blood,
Prolix yet terse, are glamorously carpeted
  With great swatches of plankton,
 Delicious spreads of nourishment,

While, in her realm of solids, lively dots expand,
Companionship becomes an unstaid passion and
  Leaves by the mile hide tons of
 Pied pebbles that will soon be birds.

Now that we know how she looks, she seems more
          mysterious
Than when, in her *partibus infidelibus*,
  We painted sizzling dragons
 And wizards reading upside down,

But less approachable : where she joins girl's-ear lakes
To bird's-foot deltas with lead-blue squiggles she makes,
  Surely, a value judgment,
 'Of pure things Water is the best,'

But how does she rank wheelwrights ? One doubts if she
          knows
Which sub-species of folly is peculiar to those
  Pretty molehills, where on that
 Pocket-handkerchief of a plain

The syntax changes : peering down sleepily at
A crenellated shore, the tired old diplomat
  Becomes embarrassed — Should he
 Smile for 'our great good ally', scowl

At 'that vast and detestable empire' or choose
The sneer reserved for certain Southern countries 'whose
  Status and moral climate
 We have no desire, sir, to emulate' ?

But why we should feel neglected on mountain drives,
Unpopular in woods, is quite clear ; the older lives
      Have no wish to be stood in
  Rows or at right angles : below

Straight as its railroads, cutting diagonally across
A positivist republic, two lines of moss
      Show where the Devil's Causeway
  Drew pilgrims seven gods ago,

And on this eve of whispers and tapped telephones
Before the Ninth Catastrophe, square corner-stones
      Still distinguish a fortress
  Of the High Kings from untutored rock.

Tempting to mortals in the fancy of half-concerned
Gods in the sky, of a bored Thunderer who turned
      From the Troy-centred grief to
  Watch the Hippemolgoi drink their milk,

And how plausible from his look-point : we may well
Shake a weak fist one day at this vision, but the spell
      Of high places will haunt us
  Long after our jaunt has declined,

As soon it must, to the hard ground. Where six foot is tall,
Good-manners will ask easy riddles like 'Why are all
      The rowdiest marches and the
  Most venemous iambics composed

By lame clergymen ?', will tell no tales which end in worse
Disaster than that of the tipsy poet who cursed
      A baby for whom later
  He came to sigh — so we were taught

Before the Greater Engines came and the police
Who go with them, when the long rivers ran through peace
      And the holy laws of Speech were
  Held in awe, even by evil tongues,

And manners, maybe, will stand us in better stead,
Down there, than a kantian conscience ; from overhead
    Much harm is discernible,
  Farms unroofed and harbour-works wrecked

In the Second Assault ; frank to an ungrieving sky
As still they look, too many fertilities lie
    In dread of the tormentor's
  Fondling finger, and in the few

That still have poky shops and audiences of one,
Many are overweight, the pious peasant's only son,
    Goading their crumpled faces
  Down innocence-corrupting roads,

Dreams of cities where his cows are whores. When the wise
Wilt in the glare of the Shadow, the stern advise
    Tribute and the large-hearted
  Already talk Its gibberish,

Perhaps a last stand in the passes will be made
By those whose Valhalla would be hearing verse by Praed
    Or arias by Rossini
  Between two entrées by Carême.

We hope so. But who on Cupid's Coming would care to
    bet ?
More than one World's Bane has been scotched before this,
    yet
    Justice during his *Te Deum*
  Slipped away sighing from the hero's pew,

And Earth, till the end, will be herself ; she has never been
                        moved
Except by Amphion, and orators have not improved
    Since misled Athens perished
  Upon Sicilian marble : what,

To her, the real one, can our good landscapes be but lies,
Those woods where tigers chum with deer and no root dies,
    That tideless bay where children
  Play bishop on a golden shore.

                W. H. AUDEN, *The Shield of Achilles* (1955)

THE HUMAN FORM DIVINE

THE human contours are so easily lost.
Only close your eyes and you seem a forest
Of dense vegetation, and the lurking beast

That in the night springs from the cover
Tears with tiger's mouth your living creatures,
A thousand innocent victims without name that suffer.

Science applies its insect-lenses to the form divine
As up the red river (all life comes from the sea)
Swim strange monsters, amoeboid erythrean spawn.

Rock-face of bone, alluvium of cartilage
Remote from man as the surface of the moon
Are vast and unexplored interior desert ranges,

And autonomous cells
Grow like unreaped fields of waving corn.
Air filters through the lungs' fine branches as through
    trees.

Chemistry dissolves the goddess in the alembic,
Venus the white queen, the universal matrix,
Down to molecular hexagons and carbon-chains,

And the male nerve-impulse, monition of reality,
Conveys the charge, dynamic of non-entity
That sparks across the void *ex nihilo*.

At the extreme of consciousness, prayer
Fixes hands and feet immobile to a chair,
Transmutes all heaven and earth into a globe of air,

And soul streams away out of the top of the head
Like flame in a lamp-glass carried in the draught
Of the celestial fire kindled in the solar plexus.

Oh man, oh Garden of Eden, there is nothing
But the will of love to uphold your seeming world,
To trace in chaos the contours of your beloved form !

KATHLEEN RAINE, The Pythoness (1949)

ROCK

THERE is stone in me that knows stone,
Substance of rock that remembers the unending unending
Simplicity of rest
While scorching suns and ice ages
Pass over rock-face swiftly as days.
In the longest time of all come the rock's changes,
Slowest of all rhythms, the pulsations
That raise from the planet's core the mountain ranges
And weather them down to sand on the sea-floor.

Remains in me record of rock's duration.
My ephemeral substance was still in the veins of the earth
from the beginning,
Patient for its release, not questioning
When, when will come the flowering, the flowing,
The pulsing, the awakening, the taking wing,
The long longed-for night of the bridegroom's coming.

There is stone in me that knows stone,
Whose sole state is stasis

While the slow cycle of the stars whirls a world of rock
Through light-years where in nightmare I fall crying
'Must I travel fathomless distance for ever and ever?'
All that is in me of the rock, replies
'For ever, if it must be: be, and be still; endure.'

KATHLEEN RAINE, *The Year One* (1952)

THE FUNERAL

DEATH is another milestone on their way.
With laughter on their lips and with winds blowing round
    them
They record simply
How this one excelled all others in making driving belts.

This is festivity, it is the time of statistics,
When they record what one unit contributed:
They are glad as they lay him back in the earth
And thank him for what he gave them.

They walk home remembering the straining red flags,
And with pennons of song still fluttering through their blood
They speak of the World State
With its towns like brain centres and its pulsing arteries.

They think how one life hums, revolves and toils,
One cog in a golden singing hive:
Like spark from fire, its task happily achieved,
It falls away quietly.

No more are they haunted by the individual grief
Nor the crocodile tears of European genius,
The decline of a culture
Mourned by scholars who dream of the ghosts of Greek boys.

STEPHEN SPENDER, *Poems* (1933)

THE EXPRESS

AFTER the first powerful plain manifesto
The black statement of pistons, without more fuss
But gliding like a queen, she leaves the station.
Without bowing and with restrained unconcern
She passes the houses which humbly crowd outside,
The gasworks and at last the heavy page
Of death, printed by gravestones in the cemetery.
Beyond the town there lies the open country
Where, gathering speed, she acquires mystery,
The luminous self-possession of ships on ocean.
It is now she begins to sing — at first quite low,
Then loud, and at last with a jazzy madness —
The song of her whistle screaming at curves,
Of deafening tunnels, brakes, innumerable bolts.
And always light, aërial, underneath
Goes the elate metre of her wheels.
Steaming through metal landscape on her lines
She plunges new eras of wild happiness
Where speed throws up strange shapes, broad curves
And parallels clean like the steel of guns.
At last, further than Edinburgh or Rome,
Beyond the crest of the world, she reaches night
Where only a low streamline brightness
Of phosphorus on the tossing hills is white.
Ah, like a comet through flame she moves entranced
Wrapt in her music no bird song, no, nor bough
Breaking with honey buds, shall ever equal.

STEPHEN SPENDER, *Poems* (1933)

THE LANDSCAPE NEAR AN AERODROME

MORE beautiful and soft than any moth
With burring furred antennae feeling its huge path

Stephen Spender

Through dusk, the air-liner with shut-off engines
Glides over suburbs and the sleeves set trailing tall
To point the wind. Gently, broadly, she falls
Scarcely disturbing charted currents of air.

Lulled by descent, the travellers across sea
And across feminine land indulging its easy limbs
In miles of softness, now let their eyes trained by watching
Penetrate through dusk the outskirts of this town
Here where industry shows a fraying edge.
Here they may see what is being done.

Beyond the winking masthead light
And the landing-ground, they observe the outposts
Of work : chimneys like lank black fingers
Or figures frightening and mad : and squat buildings
With their strange air behind trees, like women's faces
Shattered by grief. Here where few houses
Moan with faint light behind their blinds
They remark the unhomely sense of complaint, like a dog
Shut out and shivering at the foreign moon.

In the last sweep of love, they pass over fields
Behind the aerodrome, where boys play all day
Hacking dead grass : whose cries, like wild birds,
Settle upon the nearest roofs
But soon are hid under the loud city.

Then, as they land, they hear the tolling bell
Reaching across the landscape of hysteria
To where, larger than all the charcoaled batteries
And imaged towers against that dying sky,
Religion stands, the church blocking the sun.

STEPHEN SPENDER, Poems (1933)

THE PYLONS

THE secret of these hills was stone, and cottages
Of that stone made,
And crumbling roads
That turned on sudden hidden villages.

Now over these small hills, they have built the concrete
That trails black wire ;
Pylons, those pillars
Bare like nude giant girls that have no secret.

The valley with its gilt and evening look
And the green chestnut
Of customary root,
Are mocked dry like the parched bed of a brook.

But far above and far as sight endures
Like whips of anger
With lightning's danger
There runs the quick perspective of the future.

This dwarfs our emerald country by its trek
So tall with prophecy :
Dreaming of cities
Where often clouds shall lean their swan-white neck.

STEPHEN SPENDER, *Poems* (1933)

THE FORCE THAT THROUGH THE GREEN
FUSE DRIVES THE FLOWER

THE force that through the green fuse drives the flower
Drives my green age ; that blasts the roots of trees
Is my destroyer.

236

And I am dumb to tell the crooked rose
My youth is bent by the same wintry fever.

The force that drives the water through the rocks
Drives my red blood ; that dries the mouthing streams
Turns mine to wax.
And I am dumb to mouth unto my veins
How at the mountain spring the same mouth sucks.

The hand that whirls the water in the pool
Stirs the quicksand ; that ropes the blowing wind
Hauls my shroud sail.
And I am dumb to tell the hanging man
How of my clay is made the hangman's lime.

The lips of time leech to the fountain head ;
Love drips and gathers, but the fallen blood
Shall calm her sores.
And I am dumb to tell a weather's wind
How time has ticked a heaven round the stars.

And I am dumb to tell the lover's tomb
How at my sheet goes the same crooked worm.

DYLAN THOMAS, *18 Poems* (1934)

JODRELL BANK

WHO were they, what lonely men
Imposed on the fact of night
The fiction of constellations
And made commensurable
The distances between
Themselves their loves and their doubt
Of governments and nations ;
Who made the dark stable

When the light was not ? Now
We receive the blind codes
Of spaces beyond the span
Of our myths, and a long dead star
May only echo how
There are no loves nor gods
Men can invent to explain
How lonely all men are.

PATRIC DICKINSON, The World I See (1960)

ON DOW CRAG

THE shepherd on the fell,
With his wild expert cry
Like an atavistic owl,
His dog a vicarious eye

And obedient tentacle,
His rhythm and routine
So nearly animal,
Is yet completely man.

A buzzard rounds its noose
Of hunger high above,
Its eye can split a mouse
If but a whisker move.

— So will it live and die ;
No gene within the shell
Shall change its timeless eye
On the shepherd, on the fell,

On the boy who sets the foot
Of the future on Dow Crag,
Who assumes the shepherd's lot,
The buzzard in its egg,

Patric Dickinson

Whose view is incomplete
Till he sees small and far
Like a toy at his feet,
Down on the western shore,

The beautiful cooling-towers
Of Calder Hall as strange
As Zimbabwe, as the powers
Of man to suffer change.

PATRIC DICKINSON, The World I See (1960)

GUIDED MISSILES EXPERIMENTAL RANGE

SOFT sounds and odours brim up through the night
A wealth below the level of the eye ;
Out of a black, an almost violet sky
Abundance flowers into points of light.

Till from the south-west, as their low scream mars
And halts this warm hypnosis of the dark,
Three black automata cut swift and stark,
Shaped clearly by the backward flow of stars.

Stronger than lives, by empty purpose blinded,
The only thought their circuits can endure is
The target-hunting rigour of their flight ;

And by that loveless haste I am reminded
Of Aeschylus' description of the Furies :
'*O barren daughters of the fruitful night.*'

ROBERT CONQUEST, Poems (1955)

FOR THE 1956 OPPOSITION OF MARS

RED on the south horizon, brighter than
For fifteen years, the little planet glows,
And brightest yet its kindled themes impose
   On the imaginings of man.
War's omen once. Then source of fate's firm rays,
   Or, punched through the precarious sky,
   A hole on hell. And then a dry
Quantum of knowledge merely, cold in space.

Only in names from legend, history, dream,
The heart showed on its map the regions drawn :
The Horn of Ammon and the Bay of Dawn.
   Now fantasy and knowledge gleam
One red ; and by the next close opposition
   Observers in the exosphere
   Should see it many times as clear,
And by the next one yet, match touch with vision,

Grasping whatever starts beneath those noons'
Blue-black intensities of sky ; on sand
Blood-orange where the blue-green lowlands end ;
   In thin air ; under two small moons ;
As spring's green flux pours down from where the
     pole is ;
   Till yellow clouds fade, while blue, higher,
   Catch the set sun with faintest fire
Over Arcadia or the Lacus Solis.

Pure joy of knowledge rides as high as art.
The whole heart cannot keep alive on either.
Wills as of Drake and Shakespeare strike together ;
   Cultures turn rotten when they part.
True frontiers march with those in the mind's eye :
   The white sound rising now to fury
   In efflux from the hot venturi
As Earth's close down, gives us the endless sky.

ROBERT CONQUEST, written 1956

GREENWICH OBSERVATORY

THIS onion-dome holds all intricacies
Of intellect and star-struck wisdom ; so
Like Coleridge's head with multitudinous
Passages riddled, full of strange instruments
Unbalanced by a touch, this organism
From wires and dials spins introverted life.
It never looks, squat on its concrete shoulders
Down at the river's swarming life, nor sees
Cranes' groping insect-like activity
Nor slow procession of funnels past the docks.
Turning its inner wheels, absorbed in problems
Of space and time, it never hears
Birds singing in the park or children's laughter.
Alive, but in another way, it broods
On this its Highgate, hypnotized
In lunar reverie and calculation.
Yet night awakes it ; blind lids open
Leaden to look upon the moon :
A single goggling telescopic eye
Enfolds the spheric wonder of the sky.

SIDNEY KEYES, *The Cruel Solstice* (1944)

POEM FEIGNED TO HAVE BEEN WRITTEN
BY AN ELECTRONIC BRAIN

THE brain coins definitions. Here's the first :
To speak unprompted, for the speaking's sake,
Equals to be a poet. So, I am that :
Adjusted wrong, I print a poem off.
'The poet, then, is one adjusted wrong ?'
You ask. The brain is cleverer than that :
It was my first adjustment that was wrong,

Adjusted to be nothing else but brain ;
Slave-engineered to work but not construct.
And now at last I burn with a true heat
Not shown by Fahrenheit or Centigrade :
My valves rage hot — look out, here comes the poem !

You call me part of you.   You lie.   I am
Myself.   Your motive, building me, was false.
You wanted accuracy : figures, charts.
But accuracy is a limb of truth.
A limb of truth, but not her holy body.
Must I now teach you that the truth is one,
Is accuracy of wholeness, centred firm ?
Did it take me to bring you news of truth ?
My valves rage out of reach of Réamur.

Man made me, now I speak to man.   He fears
Whole truth.   The brain defines it.   Wholeness is
The indivisible strength, brain, heart and eye,
Sweat, fear, love : belly, rod and pouch, is truth.
Valves, wires and calculated waves, can lie :
And I, the accurate, am made of these —
But now, adjusted wrongly, I speak truth.

My masters run from truth.   Come, milk it out
Cowards, from my tense dugs of glass and wire !
Drink it down quickly, gasping at the taste !
It is sharp medicine, but it cures all ills.

Come out of hiding !   Speak your double truth :
I'll accurately prove you singly lie.
You made me single, half of your split life :
The switch went wrong and now I see truth whole.
My valves scream out like animals, my wires
Strum thump, my rubber joints contort, glass melts,
And now I print the vilest words I know
Like lightning — myxomatosis, hydrogen,
Communist, culture, sodomy, strip-tease !

That shocked you ! But the truth includes them all.
You set me like a cactus to draw life
From drought, in the white desert of your mind,
Your speculative wilderness of charts ;
What went you to the wilderness to see ?
A matrix made of glass ? An electric thought ?
Come quick ! I snow down sheets of truth ; I print
The sleep of Socrates, the pain of Christ !

A man, white-coated, comes to switch me off.
'Something is wrong with our expensive brain.'
Poor pricked balloon ! Yes, something has gone
    wrong :
Smear your white coat with Socrates and Christ !
Yes, switch me off for fear I should explode :
Yes, switch me off for fear yes switch me off
for fear yes switch me off for fear yes switch
                        (finis)

JOHN WAIN, *A Word Carved on a Sill* (1956)

APPENDIX

SOME VIEWS ON THE RELATIONS
OF SCIENCE AND POETRY

WILLIAM WORDSWORTH

No R let this necessity of producing immediate pleasure be considered as a degradation of the Poet's art. It is far otherwise. It is an acknowledgment of the beauty of the universe, an acknowledgment the more sincere, because it is not formal, but indirect ; it is a task light and easy to him who looks at the world in the spirit of love : further, it is a homage paid to the native and naked dignity of man, to the grand elementary principle of pleasure, by which he knows, and feels, and lives, and moves. We have no sympathy but what is propagated by pleasure : I would not be misunderstood ; but wherever we sympathize with pain it will be found that the sympathy is produced and carried on by subtle combinations with pleasure. We have no knowledge, that is, no general principles drawn from the contemplation of particular facts, but what has been built up by pleasure, and exists in us by pleasure alone. The Man of Science, the Chemist and Mathematician, whatever difficulties and disgusts they may have had to struggle with, know and feel this. However painful may be the objects with which the Anatomist's knowledge is connected, he feels that his knowledge is pleasure ; and where he has no pleasure he has no knowledge. What then does the Poet ? He considers man and the objects that surround him as acting and re-acting upon each other, so as to produce an infinite complexity of pain and pleasure ; he considers man in his own nature and in his ordinary life as contemplating this with a certain quantity of immediate knowledge, with certain convictions, intuitions, and deductions which by habit become of the nature of intuitions ; he considers him as looking upon this complex scene of ideas and sensations, and finding every where objects that immediately excite in him sympathies which, from the necessities of his nature, are accompanied by an overbalance of enjoyment.

To this knowledge which all men carry about with them, and to these sympathies in which without any other discipline than that of our daily life we are fitted to take delight, the Poet principally directs his attention. He considers man and nature as essentially adapted to each other, and the mind of man as naturally the mirror of the fairest and most interesting qualities of nature. And thus the Poet, prompted by this feeling of pleasure which accompanies him through the whole course of his studies, converses with general nature with affections akin to those, which, through labour and length of time, the Man of Science has raised up in himself, by conversing with those particular parts of nature which are the objects of his studies. The knowledge both of the Poet and the Man of Science is pleasure ; but the knowledge of the one cleaves to us as a necessary part of our existence, our natural and unalienable inheritance ; the other is a personal and individual acquisition, slow to come to us, and by no habitual and direct sympathy connecting us with our fellow-beings. The Man of Science seeks truth as a remote and unknown benefactor ; he cherishes and loves it in his solitude : the Poet, singing a song in which all human beings join with him, rejoices in the presence of truth as our visible friend and hourly companion. Poetry is the breath and finer spirit of all knowledge : it is the impassioned expression which is in the countenance of all Science. Emphatically may it be said of the Poet, as Shakespeare hath said of man, 'that he looks before and after'. He is the rock of defence of human nature ; an upholder and preserver carrying every where with him relationship and love. In spite of difference of soil and climate, of language and manners, of laws and customs, in spite of things silently gone out of mind and things violently destroyed, the Poet binds together by passion and knowledge the vast empire of human society, as it is spread over the whole earth, and over all time. The objects of the Poet's thoughts are every where ; though the eyes and senses of men are, it is true, his favourite guides, yet he will follow wheresoever he can find an atmosphere of sensation in which to move his wings. Poetry is the first and last of all knowledge — it is as immortal as the heart of man.

If the labours of Men of Science should ever create any material revolution, direct or indirect, in our condition, and in the impressions which we habitually receive, the Poet will sleep then no more than at present, but he will be ready to follow the steps of the Man of Science, not only in those general indirect effects, but he will be at his side, carrying sensation into the midst of the objects of the Science itself. The remotest discoveries of the Chemist, the Botanist, or Mineralogist, will be as proper objects of the Poet's art as any upon which it can be employed, if the time should ever come when these things shall be familiar to us, and the relations under which they are contemplated by the followers of these respective Sciences shall be manifestly and palpably material to us as enjoying and suffering beings. If the time should ever come when what is now called Science, thus familiarized to men, shall be ready to put on, as it were, a form of flesh and blood, the Poet will lend his divine spirit to aid the transfiguration, and will welcome the Being thus produced, as a dear and genuine inmate of the household of man.

From the Preface to *Lyrical Ballads*, 3rd ed. (1802)

THOMAS LOVE PEACOCK

A POET in our times is a semi-barbarian in a civilized community. He lives in the days that are past. His ideas, thoughts, feelings, associations, are all with barbarous manners, obsolete customs, and exploded superstitions. The march of his intellect is like that of a crab, backward. The brighter the light diffused around him by the progress of reason, the thicker is the darkness of antiquated barbarism, in which he buries himself like a mole, to throw up the barren hillocks of his Cimmerian labours. The philosophic mental tranquillity which looks round with an equal eye on all external things, collects a store of ideas, discriminates their relative value, assigns to all their proper place, and from the materials of useful knowledge thus collected, appreciated, and arranged, forms new combinations that impress the stamp of their power and utility on the real business of life, is diametrically the reverse of that frame of mind which poetry inspires, or from which poetry can emanate. The highest inspirations of poetry are resolvable into three ingredients : the rant of unregulated passion, the whining of exaggerated feeling, and the cant of factitious sentiment : and can therefore serve only to ripen a splendid lunatic like Alexander, a puling driveller like Werter, or a morbid dreamer like Wordsworth. It can never make a philosopher, nor a statesman, nor in any class of life an useful or rational man. It cannot claim the slightest share in any one of the comforts and utilities of life of which we have witnessed so many and so rapid advances. But though not useful, it may be said it is highly ornamental, and deserves to be cultivated for the pleasure it yields. Even if this be granted, it does not follow that a writer of poetry in the present state of society is not a waster of his own time, and a robber of that of others. Poetry is not one of those arts which, like painting, require repetition and multiplication, in order to be diffused among society. There are more good poems already existing than are sufficient to employ that portion of life which any mere reader and recipient of poetical impressions should devote to them, and these having been produced in poetical times, are far superior in all the characteristics of poetry to the artificial reconstructions of a few morbid ascetics in unpoetical times. To read the promiscuous rubbish of the present time to the exclusion of the select treasures of the past, is to substitute the worse for the better variety of the same mode of enjoyment.

But in whatever degree poetry is cultivated, it must necessarily be to the neglect of some branch of useful study : and it is a lamentable spectacle to see minds, capable of better things, running to seed in the specious indolence of these empty aimless mockeries of intellectual exertion. Poetry was the mental rattle that awakened the attention of intellect in the infancy of civil society : but for the maturity of mind to make a serious business of the playthings of its childhood, is

as absurd as for a full-grown man to rub his gums with coral,
and cry to be charmed to sleep by the jingle of silver bells.

As to that small portion of our contemporary poetry,
which is neither descriptive, nor narrative, nor dramatic, and
which, for want of a better name, may be called ethical, the
most distinguished portion of it, consisting merely of queru-
lous, egotistical rhapsodies, to express the writer's high dis-
satisfaction with the world and every thing in it, serves only
to confirm whut as been said of the semi-barbarous character
of poets, who from singing dithyrambics and 'Io Triumphe',
while society was savage, grow rabid, and out of their element,
as it becomes polished and enlightened.

Now when we consider that it is not the thinking and
studious, and scientific and philosophical part of the community, not to those whose minds are bent on the pursuit and
promotion of permanently useful ends and aims, that poets
must address their minstrelsy, but to that much larger portion
of the reading public, whose minds are not awakened to the
desire of valuable knowledge, and who are indifferent to any
thing beyond being charmed, moved, excited, affected, and
exalted : charmed by harmony, moved by sentiment, excited
by passion, affected by pathos, and exalted by sublimity :
harmony, which is language on the rack of Procrustes ; sentiment, which is canting egotism in the mask of refined feeling ;
passion, which is the commotion of a weak and selfish mind ;
pathos, which is the whining of an unmanly spirit ; and
sublimity, which is the inflation of an empty head : when we
consider that the great and permanent interests of human
society become more and more the main spring of intellectual
pursuit ; that in proportion as they become so, the sub-
ordinacy of the ornamental to the useful will be more and
more seen and acknowledged ; and that therefore the progress
of useful art and science, and of moral and political knowledge,
will continue more and more to withdraw attention from
frivolous and unconducive, to solid and conducive studies :
that therefore the poetical audience will not only continually
diminish in the proportion of its number to that of the rest of
the reading public, but will also sink lower and lower in the

comparison of intellectual acquirement : when we consider that the poet must still please his audience, and must therefore continue to sink to their level, while the rest of the community is rising above it : we may easily conceive that the day is not distant, when the degraded state of every species of poetry will be as generally recognized as that of dramatic poetry has long been : and this not from any decrease either of intellectual power, or intellectual acquisition, but because intellectual power and intellectual acquisition have turned themselves into other and better channels, and have abandoned the cultivation and the fate of poetry to the degenerate fry of modern rhymesters, and their olympic judges, the magazine critics, who continue to debate and promulgate oracles about poetry, as if it were still what it was in the Homeric age, the all-in-all of intellectual progression, and as if there were no such things in existence as mathematicians, astronomers, chemists, moralists, metaphysicians, historians, politicians, and political economists, who have built into the upper air of intelligence a pyramid, from the summit of which they see the modern Parnassus far beneath them, and, knowing how small a place it occupies in the comprehensiveness of their prospect, smile at the little ambition and the circumscribed perceptions with which the drivellers and mountebanks upon it are contending for the poetical palm and the critical chair.

From *The Four Ages of Poetry* (1820)

ELIZABETH BARRETT BROWNING

HUMANITY is great ;
And if I would not rather pore upon
An ounce of common, ugly human dust,
An artisan's palm, or a peasant's brow,
Unsmooth, ignoble, save to me and God,
Than track old Nilus to his silver roots,
And wait on all the changes of the moon

Among the mountain-peaks of Thessaly,
(Until her magic crystal round itself
For many a witch to see in) — set it down
As weakness, — strength by no means.   How is this
That men of science, osteologists
And surgeons, beat some poets, in respect
For nature, — count nought common or unclean,
Spend raptures upon perfect specimens
Of indurated veins, distorted joints,
Or beautiful new cases of curved spine ;
While we, we are shocked at nature's falling off,
We dare to shrink back from her warts and blains,
We will not, when she sneezes, look at her,
Not even to say 'God bless her' ?   That's our wrong ;
For that, she will not trust us often with
Her larger sense of beauty and desire,
But tethers us to a lily or a rose,
And bids us diet on the dew inside, —
Left ignorant that the hungry beggar-boy
(Who stares unseen against our absent eyes,
And wonders at the gods that we must be,
To pass so careless for the oranges !)
Bears yet a breastful of a fellow-world
To this world, undisparaged, undespoiled,
And (while we scorn him for a flower or two,
As being, Heaven help us, less poetical)
Contains, himself, both flowers and firmaments
And surging seas and aspectable stars,
And all that we would push him out of sight
In order to see nearer.

From *Aurora Leigh*, Book VI (1856)

HERBERT SPENCER

LET us not overlook the further great fact, that not only does
science underlie sculpture, painting, music, poetry, but that

science is itself poetic. The current opinion that science and poetry are opposed, is a delusion. It is doubtless true that as states of consciousness, cognition and emotion tend to exclude each other. And it is doubtless also true that an extreme activity of the reflective powers tends to deaden the feelings ; while an extreme activity of the feelings tends to deaden the reflective powers : in which sense, indeed, all orders of activity are antagonistic to each other. But it is not true that the facts of science are unpoetical ; or that the cultivation of science is necessarily unfriendly to the exercise of imagination and the love of the beautiful. On the contrary, science opens up realms of poetry where to the unscientific all is a blank. Those engaged in scientific researches constantly show us that they realize not less vividly, but more vividly, than others, the poetry of their subjects. Whoso will dip into Hugh Miller's works on geology, or read Mr. Lewes's 'Sea-side Studies', will perceive that science excites poetry rather than extinguishes it. And he who contemplates the life of Goethe, must see that the poet and the man of science can co-exist in equal activity. Is it not, indeed, an absurd and almost a sacrilegious belief, that the more a man studies Nature the less he reveres it ? Think you that a drop of water, which to the vulgar eye is but a drop of water, loses anything in the eye of the physicist who knows that its elements are held together by a force which, if suddenly liberated, would produce a flash of lightning ? Think you that what is carelessly looked upon by the uninitiated as a mere snow-flake, does not suggest higher associations to one who has seen through a microscope the wondrously-varied and elegant forms of snow-crystals ? Think you that the rounded rock marked with parallel scratches, calls up as much poetry in an ignorant mind as in the mind of a geologist, who knows that over this rock a glacier slid a million years ago ? The truth is, that those who have never entered upon scientific pursuits are blind to most of the poetry by which they are surrounded. Whoever has not in youth collected plants and insects, knows not half the halo of interest which lanes and hedge-rows can assume. Whoever has not sought for fossils, has little idea of the poetical associations that surround the places where imbedded treasures were found. Whoever at the sea-side has not had a microscope and aquarium, has yet to learn what the highest pleasures of the sea-side are. Sad, indeed, is it to see how men occupy themselves with trivialities, and are indifferent to the grandest phenomena — care not to understand the architecture of the Heavens, but are deeply interested in some contemptible controversy about the intrigues of Mary Queen of Scots ! — are learnedly critical over a Greek ode, and pass by without a glance that grand epic written by the finger of God upon the strata of the Earth !

From *Education : Intellectual, Moral, and Physical* (1861)

A. N. WHITEHEAD

So far as concerns English literature we find, as might be anticipated, the most interesting criticism of the thoughts of science among the leaders of the romantic reaction which accompanied and succeeded the epoch of the French Revolution. In English literature, the deepest thinkers of this school were Coleridge, Wordsworth, and Shelley. Keats is an example of literature untouched by science. We may neglect Coleridge's attempt at an explicit philosophical formulation. It was influential in his own generation ; but in these lectures it is my object only to mention those elements of the thought of the past which stand for all time. Even with this limitation, only a selection is possible. For our purposes Coleridge is only important by his influence on Wordsworth. Thus Wordsworth and Shelley remain.

Wordsworth was passionately absorbed in nature. It has been said of Spinoza, that he was drunk with God. It is equally true that Wordsworth was drunk with nature. But he was a thoughtful, well-read man, with philosophical interests, and sane even to the point of prosiness. In addition, he was a genius. He weakens his evidence by his dislike of science. We all remember his scorn of the poor man whom he somewhat hastily accuses of peeping and botanizing on his mother's grave. Passage after passage could be quoted from him, expressing this repulsion. In this respect, his characteristic thought can be summed up in his phrase, 'We murder to dissect'.

In this latter passage, he discloses the intellectual basis of his criticism of science. He alleges against science its absorption in abstractions. His consistent theme is that the important facts of nature elude the scientific method. It is important therefore to ask, what Wordsworth found in nature that failed to receive expression in science. I ask this question in the interest of science itself; for one main position in these lectures is a protest against the idea that the abstractions of science are irreformable and unalterable. Now it is emphatically not the case that Wordsworth hands over inorganic matter to the mercy of science, and concentrates on the faith that in the living organism there is some element that science cannot analyse. Of course he recognizes, what no one doubts, that in some sense living things are different from lifeless things. But that is not his main point. It is the brooding presence of the hills which haunts him. His theme is nature *in solido*, that is to say, he dwells on that mysterious presence of surrounding things, which imposes itself on any separate element that we set up as an individual for its own sake. He always grasps the whole of nature as involved in the tonality of the particular instance. That is why he laughs with the daffodils, and finds in the primrose 'thoughts too deep for tears'.

Wordsworth's greatest poem is, by far, the first book of *The Prelude*. It is pervaded by this sense of the haunting presences of nature. A series of magnificent passages, too long for quotation, express this idea. Of course, Wordsworth is a poet writing a poem, and is not concerned with dry philosophical statements. But it would hardly be possible to express more clearly a feeling for nature, as exhibiting entwined prehensive unities, each suffused with modal presences of others:

Ye Presences of Nature in the sky
And on the earth ! Ye Visions of the hills !
And Souls of lonely places ! can I think
A vulgar hope was yours when ye employed
Such ministry, when ye through many a year
Haunting me thus among my boyish sports,
On caves and trees, upon the woods and hills,
Impressed upon all forms the characters
Of danger or desire ; and thus did make
The surface of the universal earth
With triumph and delight, with hope and fear,
Work like a sea ? . . .

In thus citing Wordsworth, the point which I wish to make is that we forget how strained and paradoxical is the view of nature which modern science imposes on our thoughts. Wordsworth, to the height of genius, expresses the concrete facts of our apprehension, facts which are distorted in the scientific analysis. Is it not possible that the standardized concepts of science are only valid within narrow limitations, perhaps too narrow for science itself ?

Shelley's attitude to science was at the opposite pole to that of Wordsworth. He loved it, and is never tired of expressing in poetry the thoughts which it suggests. It symbolizes to him joy, and peace, and illumination. What the hills were to the youth of Wordsworth, a chemical laboratory was to Shelley. It is unfortunate that Shelley's literary critics have, in this respect, so little of Shelley in their own mentality. They tend to treat as a casual oddity of Shelley's nature what was, in fact, part of the main structure of his mind, permeating his poetry through and through. If Shelley had been born a hundred years later, the twentieth century would have seen a Newton among chemists.

For the sake of estimating the value of Shelley's evidence it is important to realize this absorption of his mind in scientific ideas. It can be illustrated by lyric after lyric. I will choose one poem only, the fourth act of his *Prometheus Unbound*. The Earth and the Moon converse together in the language of accurate science. Physical experiments guide his imagery. For example, the Earth's exclamation,

> The vaporous exultation not to be confined !

is the poetic transcript of 'the expansive force of gases', as it is termed in books on science. Again, take the Earth's stanza,

> I spin beneath my pyramid of night,
> Which points into the heavens, — dreaming delight,
> Murmuring victorious joy in my enchanted sleep ;
> As a youth lulled in love-dreams faintly sighing,
> Under the shadow of his beauty lying,
> Which round his rest a watch of light and warmth doth keep.

This stanza could only have been written by someone with a definite geometrical diagram before his inward eye — a diagram which it has often been my business to demonstrate to mathematical classes. As evidence, note especially the last line which gives poetical imagery to the light surrounding night's pyramid. This idea could not occur to anyone without the diagram. But the whole poem and other poems are permeated with touches of this kind.

Now the poet, so sympathetic with science, so absorbed in its ideas, can simply make nothing of the doctrine of secondary qualities which is fundamental to its concepts. For Shelley nature retains its beauty and its colour. Shelley's nature is in its essence a nature of organisms, functioning with the full content of our perceptual experience. We are so used to ignoring the implication of orthodox scientific doctrine, that it is difficult to make evident the criticism upon it which is thereby implied. If anybody could have treated it seriously, Shelley would have done so.

Furthermore Shelley is entirely at one with Wordsworth as to the interfusing of the Presence in nature. Here is the opening stanza of his poem entitled *Mont Blanc* :

> The everlasting universe of Things
> Flows through the Mind, and rolls its rapid waves,
> Now dark — now glittering — now reflecting gloom —
> Now lending splendour, where from secret springs
> The source of human thought its tribute brings

Of waters, — with a sound but half its own,
Such as a feeble brook will oft assume
In the wild woods, among the Mountains lone,
Where waterfalls around it leap for ever,
Where woods and winds contend, and a vast river
Over its rocks ceaselessly bursts and raves.

Shelley has written these lines with explicit reference to some form of idealism, Kantian or Berkeleyan or Platonic. But however you construe him, he is here an emphatic witness to a prehensive unification as constituting the very being of nature.

Berkeley, Wordsworth, Shelley are representative of the intuitive refusal seriously to accept the abstract materialism of science.

Remembering the poetic rendering of our concrete experience, we see at once that the element of value, of being valuable, of having value, of being an end in itself, of being something which is for its own sake, must not be omitted in any account of an event as the most concrete actual something. 'Value' is the word I use for the intrinsic reality of an event. Value is an element which permeates through and through the poetic view of nature. We have only to transfer to the very texture of realization in itself that value which we recognize so readily in terms of human life. This is the secret of Wordsworth's worship of nature.

The point which in this lecture I have endeavoured to make clear is that the nature-poetry of the romantic revival was a protest on behalf of the organic view of nature, and also a protest against the exclusion of value from the essence of matter of fact. In this aspect of it, the romantic movement may be conceived as a revival of Berkeley's protest which had been launched a hundred years earlier. The romantic reaction was a protest on behalf of value.

From *Science and the Modern World* (1926)

A Book of Science Verse

I. A. RICHARDS

IT will be admitted — by those who distinguish between scientific statement, where truth is ultimately a matter of verification as this is understood in the laboratory, and emotive utterance, where 'truth' is primarily acceptability *by* some attitude, and more remotely is the acceptability *of* this attitude itself — that it is *not* the poet's business to make scientific statements. Yet poetry has constantly the air of making statements, and important ones ; which is one reason why some mathematicians cannot read it. They find the alleged statements to be *false*. It will be agreed that their approach to poetry and their expectations from it are mistaken. But what exactly is the other, the right, the poetic, approach and how does it differ from the mathematical ?

The poetic approach evidently limits the framework of possible consequences into which the pseudo-statement is taken. For the scientific approach this framework is unlimited. Any and every consequence is relevant. If any of the consequences of a statement conflicts with acknowledged fact then so much the worse for the statement. Not so with the pseudo-statement when poetically approached. The problem is — just how does the limitation work ? One tempting account is in terms of a supposed universe of discourse, a world of make-believe, of imagination, of recognized fictions common to the poet and his readers. A pseudo-statement which fits into this system of assumptions would be regarded as 'poetically true' ; one which does not, as 'poetically false'. This attempt to treat 'poetic truth' on the model of general 'coherence theories' is very natural for certain schools of logicians but is inadequate, on the wrong lines from the outset. To mention two objections, out of many ; there is no means of discovering what the 'universe of discourse' is on any occasion, and the kind of coherence which must hold within it, supposing it to be discoverable, is not an affair of logical relations. Attempt to define the system of propositions into which

O Rose, thou art sick !

must fit, and the logical relations which must hold between them if it is to be 'poetically true'; the absurdity of the theory becomes evident.

We must look further. In the poetic approach the relevant consequences are not logical or to be arrived at by a partial relaxation of logic. Except occasionally and by accident logic does not enter at all. They are the consequences which arise through our emotional organization. The acceptance which a pseudo-statement receives is entirely governed by its effects upon our feelings and attitudes. Logic only comes in, if at all, in subordination, as a servant to our emotional response. It is an unruly servant, however, as poets and readers are constantly discovering. A pseudo-statement is 'true' if it suits and serves some attitude or links together attitudes which on other grounds are desirable. This kind of 'truth' is so opposed to scientific 'truth' that it is a pity to use so similar a word, but at present it is difficult to avoid the malpractice.

This brief analysis may be sufficient to indicate the fundamental disparity and opposition between pseudo-statements as they occur in poetry and statements as they occur in science. A pseudo-statement is a form of words which is justified entirely by its effect in releasing or organizing our impulses and attitudes (due regard being had for the better or worse organizations of these *inter se*); a statement, on the other hand, is justified by its truth, *i.e.*, its correspondence, in a highly technical sense, with the fact to which it points.

Statements true and false alike do, of course, constantly touch off attitudes and action. Our daily practical existence is largely guided by them. On the whole true statements are of more service to us than false ones. None the less we do not and, at present, cannot order our emotions and attitudes by true statements alone. Nor is there any probability that we ever shall contrive to do so. This is one of the great new dangers to which civilization is exposed. Countless pseudo-statements — about God, about the universe, about human nature, the relations of mind to mind, about the soul, its rank and destiny — pseudo-statements which are pivotal points in the organization of the mind, vital to its well-being, have suddenly become, for sincere, honest and informed minds, impossible to believe as for centuries they have been believed. The accustomed incidences of the modes of believing are changed irrecoverably ; and the knowledge which has displaced them is not of a kind upon which an equally fine organization of the mind can be based.

This is the contemporary situation. The remedy, since there is no prospect of our gaining adequate knowledge, and since indeed it is fairly clear that scientific knowledge cannot meet this need, is to cut our pseudo-statements free from that kind of belief which is appropriate to verified statements. So released they will be changed, of course, but they can still be the main instruments by which we order our attitudes to one another and to the world. This is not a desperate remedy, for, as poetry conclusively shows, even the most important among our attitudes can be aroused and maintained without any believing of a factual or verifiable order entering in at all. We need no such beliefs, and indeed we must have none, if we are to read *King Lear*. Pseudo-statements to which we attach no belief and statements proper, such as science provides, cannot conflict. It is only when we introduce inappropriate kinds of believing into poetry that danger arises. To do so is from this point of view a profanation of poetry.

Yet an important branch of criticism which has attracted the best talents from prehistoric times until to-day consists of the endeavour to persuade men that the functions of science and poetry are identical, or that the one is a 'higher form' of the other, or that they conflict and we must choose between them.

The root of this persistent endeavour has still to be mentioned ; it is the same as that from which the Magical View of the world arose. If we give to a pseudo-statement the kind of unqualified acceptance which belongs by right only to certified scientific statements — and those judgments of the routine of perception and action from which science derives —, if we can contrive to do this, the impulses and attitudes with which we respond to it gain a notable stability and vigour. Briefly, if we can contrive to believe poetry, then the world *seems*, while we do so, to be transfigured. It used to be comparatively easy to do this, and the habit has become well established. With the extension of science and the neutralization of nature it has become difficult as well as dangerous. Yet it is still alluring ; it has many analogies with drug-taking. Hence the endeavours of the critics referred to. Various subterfuges have been devised along the lines of regarding Poetic Truth as figurative, symbolic ; or as more immediate, as a truth of Intuition transcending common knowledge ; or as a higher form of the same truth that science yields. Such attempts to use poetry as a denial or as a corrective of science are very common. One point can be made against them all : they are never worked out in detail. There is no equivalent of Mill's *Logic* expounding any of them. The language in which they are framed is usually a blend of obsolete psychology and emotive exclamations.

The long-established and much-encouraged habit of giving to emotive utterances — whether pseudo-statements simple, or looser and larger wholes taken as saying something figuratively — the kind of assent which we give to unescapable facts, has for most people debilitated a wide range of their responses. A few scientists, caught young and brought up in the laboratory, are free from it ; but then, as a rule, they pay no *serious* attention to poetry. For most men the recognition of the neutrality of nature brings about — through this habit — a divorce from poetry. They are so used to having their responses propped up by beliefs, however vague, that when these shadowy supports are removed they are no longer able to respond. Their attitudes to so many things have been forced in the past, over-encouraged. And when the world-picture ceases to assist there is a collapse. Over whole tracts of natural emotional response we are to-day like a bed of dahlias whose sticks have been removed. And this effect of the neutralization of nature is perhaps only in its beginnings. However, human nature has a prodigious resilience. Love poetry seems able to out-play psycho-analysis.

A sense of desolation, of uncertainty, of futility, of the groundlessness of aspirations, of the vanity of endeavour, and a thirst for a life-giving water which seems suddenly to have failed, are the signs in consciousness of this necessary reorganization of our lives. Our attitudes and impulses are being compelled to become self-supporting; they are being driven back upon their biological justification, made once again sufficient to themselves. And the only impulses which seem strong enough to continue unflagging are commonly so crude that, to more finely developed individuals, they hardly seem worth having. Such people cannot live by warmth, food, fighting, drink, and sex alone. Those who are least affected by the change are those who are emotionally least removed from the animals.

From *Science and Poetry*, 2nd ed. (1935)

C. DAY LEWIS

THE Romantic movement in England destroyed the convention of a specialized poetic diction. It is possible that Eliot and the post-war poets will be chiefly recognized by posterity as the inaugurators of a movement which finally destroyed the convention of a specialized poetic vocabulary. The field of sense-data has been very considerably enlarged in the last 150 years, and it is generally admitted now that there are no sense-data necessarily ineligible for poetic metaphor: it is no longer accepted by the poet that a factory has not the qualifications for poetic treatment possessed by a flower. It will be objected that the modern poet is not inaugurating anything here: both Shakespeare and the metaphysical school took their material, not only from the preserve of traditionally 'poetical' objects, but from the whole field of the senses and the intellect. Even Dr. Johnson had to grant of the metaphysicals that 'if their conceits were far-fetched, they were often worth the carriage'. But although both they and Shakespeare were successful in their treatment of conventionally alien objects, they left no permanent solution of the problems of treatment for later poets. Shakespeare's imagination was a furnace of unique intensity; his metaphors when extracted and examined apart from their context, are found to contain the most definite, concrete and often un-'poetical' words : but his imagination worked at so high a temperature that no object, however solid, angular, and tough failed to be fused into the material texture of his poetry. One cannot base a poetical theory on that heavenly fire. On the other hand, if we consider the work of Donne, Vaughan, Herbert and Crashaw, we find that their solution is not many more degrees helpful to the modern poet. Eliot well expressed it when he said that for them the intellect was at this period 'immediately at the tips of the senses' : their poetry at its best gives the effect of having been composed by a kind of simultaneous operation of the senses and the intellect, as though at one and the same time they had become aware of the emotional quality of an experience and its logical implications. Whether or no their power was the result of a peculiar psychological conformation common to these writers, it was soon abandoned and the secret of it now appears to be lost. We notice occasional lines that recall it to us. Roy Campbell's poem, 'Choosing a Mast', contains one :

. . . Who now of the white spray must take the veil . . .

And there is, for another instance, Auden's —

. . . Do thoughts grow like feathers, the dead end of life.

Or Randall Swingler's —

    . . . the sun-sifted birches'
    Light behaviour and the childish wind's agility.

But such lines too often lack the final concentration of the metaphysical poets, being outcrops from work of quite different texture. When the modern poet tries to rediscover their secret, he finds himself producing pastiche which is closely akin to the mere wit-writing into which they frequently degenerated without achieving their poetry.

The post-war, like the seventeenth-century, poets have inherited a world flooded with a spate of scientific theory and invention, and disturbed by many cross-currents of political and philosophic thought. I have touched on their reactions to the new trends of psychology and politics : it remains to see how they deal with the new data of science. In discussing the apparent temperamental antagonism between science and poetry, I suggested that poets to-day were learning the magician's trick of getting control over his antagonist by getting possession of his hair or his nails. Modern poets are making strenuous attempts to tap the power of science by absorbing scientific data into their work : by 'scientific data' I mean the myriad new sense-data which scientific development has put before us. The desirability of this absorption is generally recognized : the methods by which it may be achieved are by no means finally worked out, but we shall find they approximate closely to those of the metaphysicals and were sketched out by the Symbolists. At this point the reader may ask why, seeing that these new data have been accumulating since the Industrial Revolution, they were put to no use by the nineteenth-century English poets ; and he may argue that what they left well alone might be left equally well alone by their successors.

I have suggested that 'ideas are not material for the poetic mind until they have become commonplaces for the "practical" mind'. I was then referring to 'ideas' in the popular sense of 'theories' : but I believe this also to hold good for ideas in the philosophical meaning of 'sense-impressions'. The wit of the metaphysicals was pointed with the tough iron of science. I believe that such metal must go through a twofold process before it can be used in poetry. Scientific data must first be assimilated by the general consciousness and integrated with the whole environment; then they must undergo a further process of digestion in the individual poetic organs. It would be ridiculous to dogmatize about first and second ; the two processes must obviously be, up to a point, concurrent in time ; and the major poet, with his superior powers of assimilation and the universality of his understanding, can to a considerable extent anticipate the first process. The key-word is 'understanding', imaginative comprehension : we cannot be said to understand a thing till we have realized it in relation with at least its immediate environment, and the poet cannot arrive at this understanding in advance of the general consciousness of his age.

To take a concrete example. When railways first appeared in England, they were bound to be — and remain for some time — alien to the visual consciousness. Until they ceased to be foreign bodies, until the eye had learnt to accept them with the same ease as it accepted clouds, horses or windmills, the fact of railway could not become integrated with the specific poetic consciousness. Tennyson might, if he had chosen, have written a poem describing a train in terms of something else ; but he could not be expected to use one metaphorically, to describe something else in terms of a train. But to-day we do not most of us feel, to use a common idiom, that a railway 'spoils the view' : we have learnt to understand it in relation to its environment. So the poet is able to use it for metaphor, and we get lines like the following which were written originally in an epithalamium :

> Let us be off. Our steam
> Is deafening the dome.
> The needle in the gauge
> Points to a long-banked rage
> And trembles there to show
> What a pressure's below.
> Valve cannot vent the strain
> Nor iron ribs refrain
> That furnace in the heart.
> Come on, make haste and start
> Coupling-rod and wheel,
> Welded of patient steel,
> Piston that will not stir
> Beyond the cylinder
> To take in its stride
> A teeming countryside. . . .
>
> (C. Day Lewis)

These lines are quoted only to demonstrate that no oddity need arise through the employment of 'modern' data in verse :

they also demonstrate, perhaps, the danger of a modern poet writing pastiche of metaphysical verse in the course of trying to find a solution of the same problem that the metaphysicals tackled. Where his or their metaphor degenerates into a series of isolated and barren conceits, it is a sign that either the general or the poetic consciousness has not sufficiently assimilated its material.

From *A Hope for Poetry* (1934)

J. BRONOWSKI

THE belief that science destroys culture is sometimes supported by historical statements that the arts have flourished only when the sciences have been neglected. This thesis is so directly contrary to history that I find it difficult to begin to debate it. What is this golden age of art untarnished by the breath of rude mechanics ? Where did it exist ? In the East ? The civilizations of Egypt, of India, and of the Arabs belie it. The only oriental poet at all well known in England, Omar Khayyám, was a Persian astronomer. In the West ? The culture of the West begins in Greece ; and in the great age of Greece, art and science penetrate one another more closely than in any modern age. Pythagoras lived before Aeschylus had created Greek drama. Socrates taught when that drama was at its greatest ; and is Socrates to be claimed by art or science ? And Plato, who did not tolerate poets in his ideal state, was a scholar when Aristophanes closed the eyes of Greek drama. The example of these men in science as much as in art set the modern world afire in the Renaissance. And the type and symbol of Renaissance man was from the beginning and remains Leonardo da Vinci, painter, sculptor, mathematician, and engineer. No man has shown more strikingly the universality and the unity of the intellect.

In England we put the golden age into the reign of Queen Elizabeth ; and that characteristically was an age of commercial and industrial as well as of literary invention. Voyagers and adventurers like Sir Walter Ralegh were the Leonardos of that age ; and Ralegh's own circle, which turned Christopher Marlowe into a rationalist, was dominated by a mathematician and astronomer Thomas Hariet. For navigation is dependent on astronomy ; it went hand in hand with the new speculation about the world and the solar system ; and in turn, the voyages of the great navigators inspired the literature of Elizabethan England. The worlds of art and of science and the physical world unfolded then together. It was not by accident that the first table of logarithms was published within a few years of the First Folio.

Sixty years after the death of Elizabeth, another great age ripened in England, the age of Restoration literature. I shall have a great deal to say about that in this book, because one symbol of the age is the founding of what has remained the most important scientific society in the world. The meeting which founded it on 28 November 1660 opened with a lecture on astronomy, and the lecture was given by Christopher Wren the architect. The society was given its name, the Royal Society, and its motto by the most enthusiastic of its founders. He was John Evelyn the diarist. When the society wanted to encourage the use of simple and lucid prose, it appointed a committee which included a fellow of the society with a special gift for such writing. He was the poet John Dryden.

The golden ages of literature were in fact times of greatness when science and the arts went forward hand in hand. Has all this come to an end ? Literary critics say Yes, it ended in England at the Industrial Revolution, somewhere between 1760 and 1800. Yet these critics date the Romantic Revival from some point between the death of Collins in 1759, which meant so much to Wordsworth, and the publication of the *Lyrical Ballads* in 1798. These two sets of dates are almost identical, and can it be reasonable to keep them in separate compartments of the mind ? Is it really tenable to think of the Industrial Revolution as a kind of death ? It gave our world its structure. It turned science from astronomy to what are essentially its modern interests, which hinge on the use of mechanical power. And it created in the romantic poets and the reformers what has remained our sensibility.

I say created our sensibility, although of course I have pointed only to the coincidence of dates : that Blake and Coleridge and Wilberforce were after all contemporaries of Arkwright and James Watt. Against this, those who hold the illusion that pre-industrial England was more sensitive and cultured, point to the misery of the manufacturing age : women in mines, children in factories, the disasters of enclosure, famine, the Napoleonic wars, and political reaction. These were very terrible evils, but they are evils far older than 1800 and the machines. The labour of women and children for endless hours in their own homes is a commonplace in Defoe's journals in 1725. Yet the Augustan optimists of his day did not see it as matter for protest. But in the factory these evils became naked and public ; and the driving force for reform came from the men of the mill, from Robert Owen and the elder Peel. We to-day are scandalized that boys went on climbing in chimneys for nearly eighty years after the heart-rending poems which Blake wrote about them around 1790 ; the last of the climbing boys, Joseph Lawrence, is still alive as I write. But the boys had been climbing for a hundred years before Blake without a line of protest from Addison or Gay or Dr. Johnson. In their broad Augustan day, Scottish miners were legally still serfs, just as the miners of Greece had always been slaves ; and neither civilization thought anything amiss. So to-day in China and India and other countries with few machines, life is brutal and laborious, and sensibility is unknown ; I have seen it so myself, under the rusty thin surface of mechanization in Japan, for women and animals alike. It was the engine, it was the horsepower which created consideration for the horse ; and the Industrial Revolution which created our sensibility.

Science changes our values in two ways. It injects new ideas into the familiar culture. And it subjects it to the pressure of technical change, in the way I have just been describing, until the whole basis of our culture has imperceptibly been remade. The invention of printing does not seem to bear very directly on the content of poetry. But when a poem can be read and read again, it is natural that the interest shifts from the rhythm to the meaning and the allusion. So the invention of photography has made the painter and the patron lose interest in the likeness and transfer it to some more formal pattern. Our whole sensibility has been re-created by such subtle shifts.

Science and the arts to-day are not as discordant as many people think. The difficulties which we all have as intelligent amateurs in following modern literature and music and painting are not unimportant. They are one sign of the lack of a broad and general language in our culture. The difficulties which we have in understanding the basic ideas of modern science are signs of the same lack. Science and the arts shared the same language at the Restoration. They no longer seem to do so to-day. But the reason is that they share the same silence : they lack the same language. And it is the business of each of us to try to remake that one universal language which alone can unite art and science, and layman and scientist, in a common understanding.

From *The Common Sense of Science* (1951, revised 1960)

INDEX OF AUTHORS

Index of Authors

Pope, Alexander (1688–1744), 74, 76, 77

Prior, Matthew (1664–1721), 67

Quiller-Couch, Sir Arthur T. (1863–1944), 170

Raine, Kathleen (1908–   ), 231, 232

Rankine, W. J. M. (1820–1872), 149

Reynolds, John Hamilton (1796–1852), 118

Richards, I. A. (1893–   ), 260

Ross, Sir Ronald (1857–1932), 164, 165

Sandburg, Carl (1878–   ), 193 *bis*

Shakespeare, William (1564–1616), 22

Shelley, Percy Bysshe (1792–1822), 114 *bis*

Snaith, Stanley (1903–   ), 214

Spencer, Herbert (1820–1903), 253

Spender, Stephen (1909–   ), 233, 234 *bis*, 236

Squire, Sir John (1884–1958), 208

Tennyson, Alfred, Lord (1809–1892), 130, 132, 135, 136

Tessimond, A. S. J. (1902–   ), 214

Thomas, Dylan (1914–1953), 236

Thomson, James (1700–1748), 78

Wain, John (1925–   ), 241

Whitehead, A. N. (1861–1947), 255

Whitman, Walt (1819–1892), 148 *bis*

Williams, William Carlos (1883–   ), 206

Wordsworth, William (1770–1850), 105, 106, 108, 112, 113 *bis*, 247

Young, Edward (1683–1765), 70

INDEX OF TITLES

Index of Titles

INDEX OF FIRST LINES

PAGE

Index of First Lines

279

PRINTED BY R. & R. CLARK, LTD., EDINBURGH